Pl

by

R. A. Penfold

BERNARD BABANI (publishing) LTD
THE GRAMPIANS
SHEPHERDS BUSH ROAD
LONDON W6 7NF
ENGLAND

Please Note

Although every care has been taken with the production of this book to ensure that any projects, designs, modifications and/or programs etc. contained herewith, operate in a correct and safe manner and also that any components specified are normally available in Great Britain, the Publishers do not accept responsibility in any way for the failure, including fault in design, of any project, design, modification or program to work correctly or to cause damage to any other equipment that it may be connected to or used in conjunction with, or in respect of any other damage or injury that may be so caused, nor do the Publishers accept responsibility in any way for the failure to obtain specified components.

Notice is also given that if equipment that is still under warranty is modified in any way or used or connected with home-built equipment then that warranty may be void.

First Published – October 1991
Reprinted – December 1994
Reprinted – June 1999

British Library Cataloguing in Publication Data
Penfold, R. A.
    Preamplifier and filter circuits.
    I. Title
    621.3893

    ISBN 0 85934 254 9

Printed and bound in Great Britain by Cox & Wyman Ltd, Reading

Contents

Preface

In the world of hobby electronics over the last thirty years or so, several areas of interest have come into fashion only to fade away again. Going against the general run of things, the construction of audio equipment seems to have maintained its popularity over this entire period. It certainly seems to be as popular now as at any time in the past, except perhaps for the early seventies when hi-fi hit an exceptional peak of popularity. Audio is one aspect of electronic project building where it is still possible to build fairly simple but very useful devices which do not cost the proverbial "arm and a leg".

This book is mainly intended for use in conjunction with "High Power Audio Amplifier Construction" (BP277), which contains designs for several power amplifiers having output powers of around 40 to 400 watts r.m.s. However, BP277 does not give details of any preamplifiers, tone controls, etc. This book provides circuits for several preamplifiers, tone controls, filters, mixers, etc., for use with power amplifiers such as those featured in BP277. It must be emphasised though, that these circuits should work equally well with any other power amplifiers, and they are quite definitely not exclusively for use with the power amplifiers in BP277.

No construction details are provided for the circuits featured in this book, and it is not really intended for complete beginners. On the other hand, the circuits are all pretty simple, and you do not really need much previous experience of electronic project construction in order to tackle them. Where appropriate, any setting up procedures and notes on tricky aspects of construction are provided.

R. A. Penfold

Chapter 1

PREAMPLIFIERS

Operational amplifier techniques seem to dominate modern preamplifier design. Even where preamplifiers are not built around true operational amplifier integrated circuits, they are usually based on specialist audio chips that are fundamentally just operational amplifiers plus some built-in biasing and feedback components. Preamplifiers based on discrete circuitry are something of a rarity these days, but even these tend to be based on what are basically operational amplifier style circuits, complete with differential inputs.

This is really not all that surprising. Operational amplifier techniques make it very easy to set any desired input impedance and voltage gain figures. Unlike many other types of audio amplifier, these figures can be set quite accurately. Using 1% resistors, which are now available quite cheaply, the error in the input impedance would be no more than 1%. The maximum error in the voltage gain would be no more than 2%. This degree of precision is not available with most other types of audio circuit, where the wide variations in the current gains of the transistors tend to give rather "hit and miss" results.

Feedback

Operational amplifiers were originally designed as d.c. amplifiers in analogue computers. They were used to perform mathematical operations, and it is from this that their name was derived. It is unlikely that many of the operational amplifiers currently produced end up in analogue computers. Computers of this type are mainly in the "museum piece" category these days. The precision they can provide though, makes them well suited to many applications, including audio, oscillator, and control applications.

These devices were designed to operate with dual balanced supplies so that they could provide positive or negative results. In some applications they are still used in this manner, but in audio applications they are mainly used with a more

1

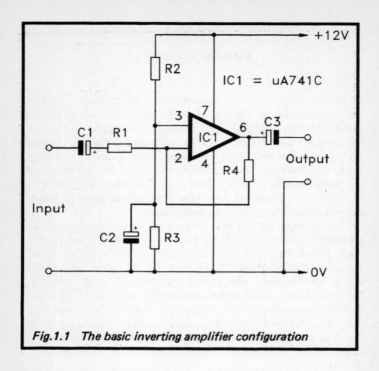

Fig.1.1 The basic inverting amplifier configuration

conventional single supply plus a bias circuit. There are two basic modes of operation, which are the inverting and non-inverting modes. As their names imply, one provides an inversion of the signal while the other has the input and output signals in-phase. The basic inverting and non-inverting amplifiers are shown in Figures 1.1 and 1.2 respectively. These are the normal audio style amplifiers, having a single supply rail and bias circuits.

The basic action of an operational amplifier is very simple indeed. It is a very high gain differential amplifier. In other words, it amplifies the voltage difference across its two inputs, but due to the very high voltage gain only a minute voltage difference is needed in order to send the output fully positive or negative. The output goes positive if the non-inverting (+) input is at a higher voltage than the inverting (−) input, or negative

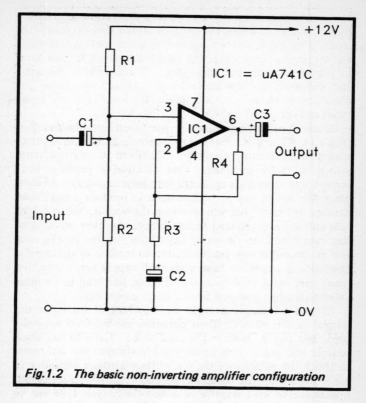

Fig.1.2   The basic non-inverting amplifier configuration

if the relative states of the two inputs are reversed. In theory an operational amplifier has infinite voltage gain, but this is obviously not achieved in practice. However, at d.c. the voltage gain is typically around 200,000 times. Note that with practical operational amplifiers the voltage gain is rolled-off at frequencies of (typically) more than about 10 KHz or so. When using these devices in audio amplifiers it has to be borne in mind that their voltage gains at high audio frequencies are often quite modest.

Such high and frequency-dependent voltage gain would seem to render operational amplifiers of little use for audio applications. The secret of success is to tame the innate (open

3

loop) voltage gain of the amplifier by applying negative feedback. This gives a much lower gain to the overall circuit (the closed loop gain), and a frequency response that is essentially flat up to the point where the gain of the device is inadequate to provide the required gain figure. It also reduces the noise and distortion to reasonable levels. In fact the noise and distortion levels are very low indeed for some specialist audio types such as the NE5534A.

If we consider operation of the inverting amplifier first (Fig.1.1), R2 and R3 bias the non-inverting input to approximately half the supply voltage. C2 is not strictly necessary, but is normally included. One function it provides is to remove any stray pick-up at the non-inverting input. In most cases this would not be high enough to produce a significant amount of "hum" (or whatever) on the output, but with high gain circuits it could lead to instability. Another function of this capacitor is to decouple any "hum" on the supply rails, and to decouple any feedback due to loading of the supply. Operational amplifiers have quite high supply ripple rejection when used with dual balanced supplies, but tend to be more vulnerable when powered from a single supply rail.

C1 and C3 simply provide d.c. blocking at the input and output of the circuit. Their polarities are the ones normally used, but one or both might need to be altered to suit some sources and loads. If in doubt you can always use a test meter to check the polarity of the d.c. voltage across a capacitor to see if it matches the component's polarity. With a high input impedance or load impedance a non-electrolytic type can be utilized. As a "rule of thumb", a value of about $2\mu2$ is suitable for a coupling capacitor that is feeding into an impedance of 10k. For higher impedances the values of the capacitor should be reduced proportionately — for lower impedances it is increased proportionately. As a couple of examples, a value of $4\mu7$ would be suitable for a 4k7 load, while a value of 470n $(0\mu47)$ would be satisfactory for a 47k load.

R1 and R4 are the negative feedback resistors. These set the closed loop voltage gain of the amplifier (i.e. its actual voltage gain). The basic action of the circuit is to stabilise the inverting input at the same voltage as the non-inverting input. If the output should drift higher in voltage, the coupling through R4 unbalances the inputs, and sends the output more negative. Any negative drift unbalances the input voltages in the opposite direction, and sends the output more positive.

An input voltage also results in the inputs becoming unbalanced, and the feedback action again corrects this. If we assume that R1 and R4 have the same value, taking the input one volt positive results in the output going one volt negative. A simple potential divider action across these two resistors then gives the required voltage at the inverting input. If R4 is made higher in value, then the output voltage must be greater in order to maintain the balance at the inputs. In other words, making R4 higher in value boosts the voltage gain of the circuit. In fact the gain of the circuit is merely equal to the value of R4 divided by that of R1.

What is termed a "virtual earth" is formed at the inverting input. In the d.c. coupled version of this configuration the non-inverting input is biased to the central 0 volt earth rail, and the feedback therefore maintains the inverting input at the earth voltage. As far as the current flow through R1 is concerned, it is much the same as if the end that connects to the inverting input really was connected to earth. Hence the term "virtual earth". With the single supply configuration the inverting input is stabilised at the half supply voltage bias level. However, with an a.c. audio input signal (such as an audio signal), the current flow through R1 is again much the same as if it was actually connected to earth.

Calculations

The practical importance of this is that the input impedance of the circuit is equal to whatever value is given to R1. This makes it very easy indeed to set the required input impedance and voltage gain figures for the circuit. The value of R1 is simply made equal to the required input impedance. The correct value for R4 is obtained by multiplying the value of R1 by the required voltage gain. For example, assume that the amplifier must have an input impedance of 50k and a voltage gain of twenty times. The correct value for R1 is 50k. This is not a preferred value, so it must either be made up from two resistors in series or parallel, or the nearest preferred value could be used. In most cases the exact input impedance of a circuit is not critical, and a value of 51k or 47k would almost certainly be perfectly satisfactory.

The correct value for R4 is 50k multiplied by twenty, which is obviously 1 megohm (1000k). There is no problem here as this is a preferred value. In most audio applications the precise voltage gain of a circuit is not critical, and it is then quite acceptable to choose the nearest value above the calculated figure where the latter is not a preferred value.

With a theoretical operational amplifier you can set any desired input impedance and voltage gain. In practice there are definite limitations though. As already pointed out, a real operational amplifier has a massive voltage gain, but only at d.c. and very low frequencies. In audio applications it is generally not possible to obtain a high voltage gain from a single operational amplifier, since its open loop voltage gain will simply not be high enough at the upper end of the audio range.

The important parameter in this context is the unity gain bandwidth of the operational amplifier. This is 1MHz for the industry standard μA741C and its many direct equivalents. Some more recent devices have higher figures, but apart from a few "specials" there are few devices which do much better than about 3MHz to 4MHz. The significance of this parameter is that you can obtain the open loop voltage gain of the device at audio frequencies by dividing the unity gain bandwidth figure by the frequencies in question. Therefore, the μA741C has a voltage gain of only fifty times at the top audio frequency of 20kHz (1MHz [1000kHz] divided by 20kHz equals 50).

More recent types, particularly the popular f.e.t input types, achieve a more useful gain at 20kHz of around 150 to 225 times. Even so, in many audio applications two stages of amplification are needed in order to obtain the required voltage gain. Bear in mind that you are unlikely to get the best from an operational amplifier if you use it at its limits. A two-stage circuit with the amplifiers used well within their maximum gain figures is likely to give much better results.

It should perhaps be pointed out that we are talking here about so-called internally compensated operational amplifiers. These are devices which have an internal capacitor which rolls-off their high frequency response. This capacitor ensures that the amplifier is stable at any gain level, right down to unity gain. Instability can be caused by stray capacitance, etc., causing phase shifts in the feedback network. These can result in the negative feedback being inverted into the positive variety, possibly causing oscillation. The compensation capacitor ensures that gain at the frequency where this inversion occurs is too low to produce oscillation.

It is important to realise that a compensation capacitor does no more than provide a circuit that is fundamentally stable. It will not necessarily ensure good stability with a circuit that has a poorly designed component layout that encourages stray feedback.

Some operational amplifiers do not have a compensation capacitor, and require a discrete capacitor or even several components in order to prevent them from becoming unstable in use. The salient point here is that the higher the closed loop voltage gain of the circuit, the lower the amount of roll-off that is required. This enables higher gain at higher frequencies to be obtained using one of these externally compensated devices.

Although the difference in performance can be quite high, externally compensated operational amplifiers do not seem to be particularly popular. The μA748C is the externally compensated version of the μA741C, and at high voltage gains this can achieve something like ten times the gain-bandwidth product of the μA741C. This enables quite high voltage gains to be obtained from a single device while retaining the full audio bandwidth, but for many purposes the noise and distortion performance would not be good enough. As pointed out previously, in audio applications two low gain stages generally offer better performance than one stage operating flat-out.

Non-Inverting

The non-inverting circuit of Figure 1.2 is similar in operation to the inverting circuit. As before, R1 and R2 bias the non-inverting input to about half the supply voltage. In this case though, no decoupling capacitor can be used because the input signal is coupled to the non-inverting input. This changes the mathematics somewhat, since the input impedance of the circuit is not governed by a resistor in the feedback network. Instead, it is equal to the parallel impedance of R1 and R2. As these resistors will have the same value in most cases, this means that the input impedance of the circuit is equal to half this value. In other words, simply make R1 and R2 equal to double the required input impedance.

This obviously assumes that the operational amplifier has an infinite input impedance, and that it will not reduce the input impedance of the circuit. In practice the input impedance of an operational amplifier will be finite, but too high to be of significance. At least, it will at low frequencies. It is worth keeping in mind that the small amount of input capacitance can drastically reduce the input impedance of a circuit at high audio frequencies. This is a factor that is common to practically all audio amplifiers, and one which can easily be ignored in practice. It tends to be of more significance in test gear and instrumentation applications.

The voltage gain of the circuit is again controlled by a two resistor negative feedback circuit (R3 and R4). At d.c. there is 100% negative feedback through R4, because C2 has an infinite resistance, and effectively cuts R3 out of the circuit. This gives unity voltage gain, and results in the output of the circuit being biased to the required level of half the supply voltage. This permits high output levels to be accommodated without the signal becoming clipped. At audio frequencies C2 has a low impedance in comparison to R3, and this reduces the amount of feedback applied to the circuit. Accordingly, the closed loop voltage gain of the amplifier is increased.

The method of calculating the voltage gain is slightly different to the method used for the inverting configuration. First add the values of R3 and R4, and then divide this figure by the value of R3. For example, if the values of R3 and R4 are respectively 10k and 100k, the voltage gain is eleven times (100k plus 10k equals 110k, 110k divided by 10k equals 11). Suitable values for R3 and R4 can be determined by first setting a likely value for R3. Something in the region of 10k is usually satisfactory, but a lower value may be necessary where high voltage gain is required. The correct value for R4 is then equal to the value of R3 multiplied by one less than the desired voltage gain. For example, for a voltage gain of twenty-five times and with R3 at a value of 10k, R4 would need to have a value of 240k (10k multiplied by (25−1) equals 240k).

When designing circuits using operational amplifiers you need to be careful when a combination of high gain and high input impedance are required. The first problem is that you may find that impractical resistor values are required. It is quite easy to end up with a circuit that requires a feedback resistor of around 100 megohms in value! Where possible it is better if feedback resistors of even a few megohms can be avoided. These leave the circuit's frequency response open to fluctuations caused by quite small stray capacitances.

Even where suitable resistors for the required gain and input impedance are a practical proposition, high gain and input impedance in a single stage are best avoided. There can be extreme difficulties with instability due to stray feedback, especially with non-inverting amplifiers (which is the mode that would probably have to be used). It is generally better to adopt a two-stage approach. The first stage provides the high input impedance together with a modest voltage gain, while the second stage provides the "lions share" of the voltage gain.

It is often necessary to incorporate a "hum" filter in the bias circuit when using the non-inverting mode. Figure 1.3 shows a non-inverting circuit which includes this facility.

R5 and C4 are the "hum" filter, and these simply form a basic lowpass filter in the supply to the bias circuit. In other respects the circuit is exactly as before. Ideally the time constant of these two components should be quite long so that they provide good attenuation of the noise. This is especially important if there is a lot of low frequency noise, such as mains "hum". In general, results will be satisfactory if multiplying the value of R5 (in kilohms) by the value of C4 (in microfarads) gives an answer of around 200 to 500. For example, values of 3k3 and 100μ should be suitable (3.3 × 100 = 330). With this type of thing though, you often have to take a "suck it and see" approach in order to find out what will give satisfactory results.

Remember that any noise which reaches the input of the amplifier will then be subjected to the full amplification of the

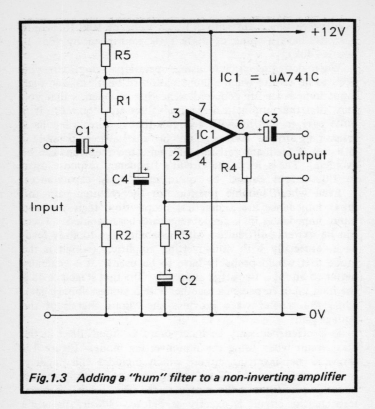

Fig.1.3 *Adding a "hum" filter to a non-inverting amplifier*

circuit. With a high gain circuit any noise which reaches the input must be kept to an extremely low level indeed if a low output noise level is to be achieved. This generally requires both a low ripple level and general noise content on the supply rail, plus a "hum" filter.

Also bear in mind that the resistor in the filter circuit alters the biasing of the circuit. Consequently, the value of this resistor must be low in comparison to that of R1 in order to minimise the error. Alternatively, the value of R1 can be reduced to compensate for the extra resistance provided by R5.

As a simple design example for a non-inverting circuit, suppose that an input impedance of about 10k plus a voltage

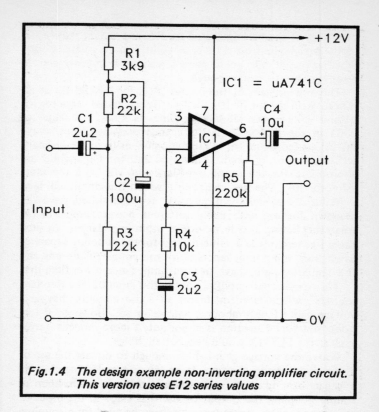

Fig.1.4 *The design example non-inverting amplifier circuit. This version uses E12 series values*

gain of about 26dB (twenty times) is required. We will also assume that "hum" filtering is required. Figure 1.4 shows an amplifier circuit which meets these requirements.

With an input impedance of 10k, the bias resistors must have a value of double this figure, or some 20k for each one. This is a preferred value in the E24 series, but 22k resistors from the E12 series will give an input impedance of 11k which should be close enough for most purposes. R1 and C2 act as the "hum" filter, and have a long enough time constant to give good low frequency attenuation. I suppose that if you require things optimised as far as possible, R2 could be reduced to 18k. This would largely remove the slight

11

offsetting of the biasing caused by R1, and would reduce the input impedance from 11k to a slightly more accurate 9k9. Whether or not this would make a noticeable improvement in results is open to doubt though.

The voltage gain of the circuit is set by R4 and R5 at 23 times. With a value of 10k for R4, the calculated value for R5 with a voltage gain of twenty times is 190k. A value of 200k in the E24 series is the nearest preferred value above the calculated figure, or a 220k component from the ordinary E12 series can be used. Values of $2\mu2$ for C1 and C3 are appropriate for the input impedance of 10k, and the same value for R4. The impedance into which the circuit will feed is frequently an unknown quantity, as preamplifiers are often designed for use with many different power amplifiers (or whatever) having a wide variety of input impedances. In such cases I generally use a value of 10μ for the coupling capacitor as this suits input impedances down to a couple of kilohms, and few amplifiers, etc., have an input impedance lower than this.

The operational amplifier used in this circuit is the standard μA741C, which is adequate for an audio amplifier having a voltage gain of only about 20 times or so. However, if low noise and (or) distortion is important, a more modern device such as the LF351N would be a better choice.

Where the voltage gain is high enough to dictate the use of a two-stage circuit, the two stages can be coupled together via a capacitor. In most cases though, there is no problem in simply coupling the output of the first stage to the input of the second stage. Apart from avoiding the need for a coupling capacitor, this usually enables the bias components for the second stage to be omitted as well. A few examples of d.c. coupled two-stage circuits are to be found further on in this chapter.

Guitar Preamplifier

Anyone who designs electronic gadgets for use with electric guitars soon learns that there is a major problem. This is simply the difference in the output levels from various guitar pick-ups. The home-made guitar pick-ups that were popular some years ago, plus possibly a few older commercially produced types, are low impedance devices which have quite low output levels. We are talking here in terms of an output signal that is only a few millivolts r.m.s. after the initial peak has subsided. Cheaper ready-made pick-ups have similar characteristics, but generally have slightly higher impedances and output levels. The more expensive units have medium output impedances and much higher output levels. In fact some guitar pick-ups apparently have output levels of around 2 volts r.m.s. after the initial peak. This is around one hundred to one thousand times higher than that of the lowest output pick-ups.

Many pieces of electronic equipment that are designed for operation with electric guitars get around this problem by having a control (possibly an internal preset) that can be set to suit practically any guitar pick-up. Others are simply designed to be able to accommodate a wide range of input levels. Despite this, users of low level guitar pick-ups can find themselves with effects units and (or) amplification equipment which will not work properly with their guitar. The opposite problem is also possible, but seems to be rare in practice. Units that are designed for only one type of guitar pick-up invariably seem to be aimed at the higher output types. If overloading should occur, a simple attenuator will solve the problem. A series resistor added in the guitar lead, possibly mounted in one of the plugs, will often suffice. Where an inadequate drive level is the problem, a simple preamplifier is required.

A suitable preamplifier circuit for this application is shown in Figure 1.5. The amount of extra gain required is not normally massive, and a single stage amplifier is therefore sufficient. This is a simple non-inverting mode circuit having an input impedance of 50k. This should suit most guitar pick-ups, but the values of C1, R1, and R2 can be altered to give a different input impedance if necessary.

The voltage gain can be varied from about four times to approximately 51 times by means of VR1. In practice this preset resistor is adjusted for the lowest gain that gives satisfactory results. The LF351N specified for the IC1 position has a gain bandwidth product of 4MHz, which is more than adequate for the full audio bandwidth (20kHz) at maximum gain. Similar devices such as the TL071CP and TL081CP will also work well in this circuit, and in the other circuits in

13

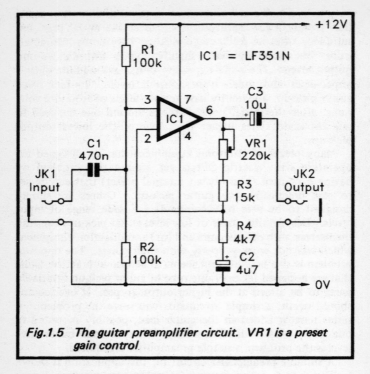

Fig.1.5 *The guitar preamplifier circuit. VR1 is a preset gain control.*

this book where an LF351N is specified.

Although the supply voltage for this circuit, and most of the others in this book, is given as 12 volts, this should be regarded as a minimum figure for good results. A 9 volt battery supply will probably give adequate results with all the circuits, but gives less "headroom". Output levels of around 3 to 4 volts r.m.s. can be handled using a 12 volt supply, but with a 9 volt supply the maximum figure is likely to be under 2 volts r.m.s. The importance of this clearly depends on the sort of output levels that will occur, and a 9 volt supply may be adequate in many cases.

Where battery operation and more headroom are required, using two batteries in series to give an 18-volt supply will probably be the simplest solution. This enables output levels of well over 5 volts r.m.s. to be achieved without clipping or serious distortion occurring. The absolute maximum operating voltage for the LF351N (and most other operational amplifiers) is 36 volts, although the maximum recommended supply voltage is lower at 30 volts. The current consumption of the guitar amplifier is only about 2 milliamps incidentally, which means that the circuit can be powered economically from one or two small 9-volt (PP3 size) batteries. No "hum" filter is included in this circuit, or any of the others in this book. Obviously such a filter should be added if the supply is not a "clean" type, such as a battery or highly smoothed mains derived supply.

Construction

Construction of this circuit should not present any major problems as it is so simple. A small piece of stripboard will accommodate everything, and there is no real need to resort to a custom printed circuit design. However, bear in mind that the circuit has a fairly high input impedance, moderately high voltage gain with VR1 at maximum resistance, and that the input and output are in-phase. Stray feedback from the output to the input can easily cause instability, and the component layout needs to be carefully designed. As explained previously, VR1 is adjusted for the lowest gain (i.e. set at the lowest resistance) that gives satisfactory results, and this is just a matter of using a bit of trial and error.

With a very low output pick-up the voltage gain of the circuit might be inadequate. If only a small boost in gain is required it is just a matter of making R3 higher in value. The output levels from a small minority of pick-ups are so low that this will not cure the problem, and for these it is necessary to use a two-stage amplifier. Using an input designed for a high impedance microphone usually gives good results, or the high impedance microphone amplifier described later in this chapter can be used between the guitar and a high level input.

In the components list for this project, and the others in this book, the resistors are specified as 5% carbon film types. This is a minimum requirement, and superior resistors such as 1% metal film types are also suitable. In fact there is some advantage in using metal film resistors in that they have lower noise levels. This could give a noticeable improvement in performance, particularly with resistors that appear at the input of high gain circuits. There is also some slight advantage in using close tolerance resistors, as they give more accurate bias levels, gain levels, etc. However, in most cases using something better than ordinary 5% tolerance carbon film resistors will not give any obvious improvement in performance. For good noise performance VR1 should be a good quality preset resistor.

Components for Figure 1.5

Resistors (all 0.25 watt 5% carbon film)
R1	100k
R2	100k
R3	15k
R4	4k7

Potentiometer
VR1	220k sub-min preset

Capacitors
C1	470n polyester
C2	4µ7 63V elect
C3	10µ 50V elect

Semiconductor
IC1	LF351N or similar

Miscellaneous
JK1	standard jack socket
JK2	standard jack socket
	8 pin d.i.l. holder, circuit board, case, etc.

Microphone Preamplifier
One characteristic that is common to practically all microphones is that they have an extremely low output level. Offhand, the only form of microphone I can think of which has a reasonably high output level is the carbon type, as used in old

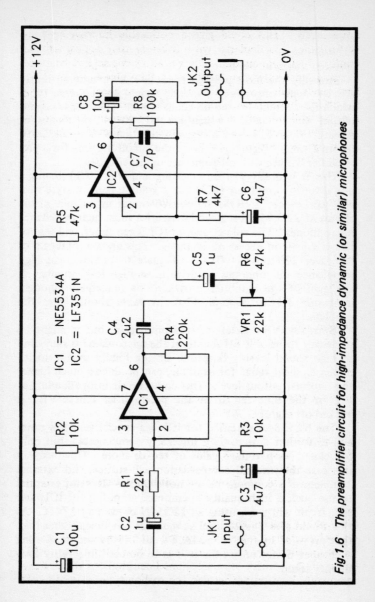

Fig.1.6 The preamplifier circuit for high-impedance dynamic (or similar) microphones

17

style (non-electronic) telephone handsets. This type of microphone is little used these days though, and we will not consider them further here.

Probably the most popular types of microphone currently are the high impedance dynamic type, and electret types which have a built-in step-up transformer. These have similar output characteristics, which are an output impedance of around 10k to 50k, and a typical output level of around 2mV to 5mV r.m.s. Figure 1.6 shows the circuit diagram for a pre-amplifier for use with microphones of either type.

This is basically just an inverting amplifier (IC1) driving a non-inverting amplifier (IC2) via a volume control style variable gain control (VR1). R1 sets the input impedance of the circuit at 22k, which is a good match for most high impedance microphones. The voltage gain of IC1 is ten times, and that of IC2 is a little in excess of 22 times. This gives a total gain of just over 220 times. This is adequate to permit most high impedance microphones to drive most high level inputs. If the gain of the amplifier proves to be inadequate though, increasing R4 to around 470k in value should cure the problem.

Normally VR1 is left at maximum gain, but it might be necessary to back it off slightly if the microphone is subjected to high sound levels. Someone singing loudly into a microphone at short range for example, can produce a much higher than normal output level. This could result in overloading of IC2 or the unit fed from the preamplifier unless VR1 is backed-off slightly.

The NE5534A specified for IC1 is a special very low noise and distortion device. It is internally compensated, but only for closed loop voltage gains of ten or more. Obviously in this case the internal compensation will suffice, and external compensation components are not required. It is not essential to use such a high quality operational amplifier for IC1, and the circuit will work using an LF351N or even a μA741C. As this would give a noise level as much as ten times higher than that provided by the NE5534A, I would not recommend using a cheaper device unless the unit is to be used in a fairly low-fidelity setup.

Although both operational amplifiers have internal compensation, this does not guarantee that the circuit as a whole will be stable. To aid good stability, C7 is used to provide extra feedback over IC2 at high frequencies above the upper limit of the audio range. This provides additional high frequency roll-off. Also, the circuit has been designed so that the input and output of the circuit are out-of-phase. This still does not guarantee freedom from instability as there are still parts of the circuit that are in-phase with other parts of the circuit. You should also bear in mind that phase shifts can occur through the stray capacitances and inductances that are responsible for stray feedback. This can turn out-of-phase feedback into in-phase feedback that can cause high frequency oscillation. The circuit can be built satisfactorily on stripboard, but reasonable care has to be taken with the layout. Having a copper strip carrying an output signal running alongside a strip carrying an input signal is not a good idea!

Another problem to keep in mind when dealing with any high gain audio circuit is that of stray pick-up of mains "hum", etc. The microphone should have a good quality screened lead that will keep stray pick-up to an insignificant level. The lead that connects JK1 to the main circuit board should also be a screened type. Alternatively, if the project is housed in a case of all-metal construction, provided this is earthed to the negative supply rail it will provide overall screening of the unit. If the lead to JK1 is kept quite short, it is then unnecessary to use a screened lead. With any sensitive audio circuit I would recommend using a metal case earthed to the negative supply rail so that the circuit board, etc., are screened. Diecast aluminium boxes are ideal for this sort of application, but any case of all-metal construction will probably give the desired effect.

Components for Figure 1.6

Resistors (all 0.25 watt 5% carbon film)

R1	22k
R2	10k
R3	10k
R4	220k
R5	47k

R6	47k
R7	4k7
R8	100k

Potentiometer

| VR1 | 22k log carbon |

Capacitors

C1	100μ 25V elect
C2	1μ 63V elect
C3	4μ7 63V elect
C4	2μ2 63V elect
C5	1μ 63V elect
C6	4μ7 63V elect
C7	27p ceramic plate
C8	10μ 50V elect

Semiconductors

| IC1 | NE5534A |
| IC2 | LF351N |

Miscellaneous

JK1	standard jack socket
JK2	standard jack socket
	Two 8 pin d.i.l. i.c. holders, circuit board, case, etc.

Low Z Microphone Preamplifier

Some high impedance dynamic microphones genuinely have high impedance coils, but many of them seem to be low impedance types with a built-in step-up transformer. Similarly, many electret microphones achieve a higher output level and higher output impedance by using an integral step-up transformer. Some dynamic and electret microphones actually offer two output impedances and output levels. These are usually the direct output and the output via the step-up transformer, although in some cases the "direct" output is actually obtained from a low impedance tapping on the transformer.

In theory there is no point in using a step-up transformer as it simply introduces signal losses. In practice it is also likely to produce some distortion and loss of frequency response. The advantage of using a step-up transformer is that it provides an output signal that is a better match for semiconductor amplifiers. Normal transistors are not at their best with low source impedances and very low signal levels. Better performance is normally obtained with higher signal levels and source impedances.

On the other hand, if a circuit that operates well with the direct signal can be produced, it does offer a potentially higher overall performance. The preamplifier circuit of Figure 1.7 is for a low impedance dynamic microphone, or one having similar output characteristics. This basically means electret microphones without a built-in step-up transformer, plus one or two unusual types which you are unlikely to encounter (certain ribbon type microphones for example).

This circuit is basically just a slight reworking of the previous circuit. The only difference is in the feedback circuit for IC1 where the values have been selected to give a higher voltage gain of 40dB (100 times) and a lower input impedance of 680 ohms. The output level from a low impedance microphone is only about one-tenth of that from a high impedance type, making it necessary to boost the gain of the input stage by a factor of ten in order to compensate for this. The lower source impedance makes it acceptable to use a lower input impedance, which gives a lower noise level from IC1.

Traditional transistor theory dictates that the noise level drops as the source impedance is reduced, until a certain ideal source impedance is reached. Decreasing the source impedance further then produces a slight increase in the noise level. My experience, and that of others, would suggest that this is not the case, and that the lower the source impedance, the lower the noise level obtained. At least, this is the case using bipolar transistors, or an integrated circuit such as the NE5534A used for IC1 which has a bipolar input stage. With f.e.t. input circuits the source impedance has little effect on the noise level.

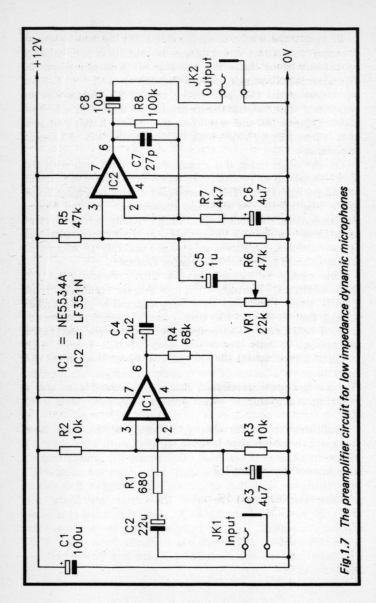

Fig. 1.7 The preamplifier circuit for low impedance dynamic microphones

IC1 = NE5534A
IC2 = LF351N

22

The practical result of all this is that the low source impedance helps to give a low noise level from IC1, and to some
extent compensates for the higher noise level caused by the
boost in its voltage gain. Together with the fact that IC1 is a
type which has a very low noise level anyway, this produces a
very acceptable noise performance from the circuit. In fact a
signal-to-noise ratio of around 80dB might be achieved, but
the precise figure depends on the output level of the microphone, the noise performance of the particular device used
for IC1, etc.

Many low impedance dynamic microphones are very much
in the "cheap and cheerful" category, and do not provide a
very high level of performance. If you are using one of these
in an application which is something less than hi-fi, you might
prefer to use a cheaper operational amplifier for IC1. Due to
the low input impedance, a f.e.t. input type such as the
LF351N is not likely to provide very good results. In this
instance an ordinary μA741C will provide superior noise
performance, but with somewhat compromised high frequency
performance. Probably the best low cost option is a μA748C
(the non-internally compensated μA741C) with an external
compensation capacitor of about 4p7 connected between pins
1 and 8. The noise level will probably be about 20dB worse
(i.e. ten times higher) than that obtained from an NE5534A
though.

Like the previous circuit, this one has high gain and is
therefore vulnerable to stray pick-up of mains "hum", etc.
Accordingly, it should be housed in a metal case to provide
overall screening, and due care should be exercised when
designing the component layout.

Components for Figure 1.7

Resistors (all 0.25 watt 5% carbon film)
R1   680R
R2   10k
R3   10k
R4   68k
R5   47k
R6   47k

| R7 | 4k7 |
| R8 | 100k |

Potentiometer
| VR1 | 22k log carbon |

Capacitors
C1	100µ 25V elect
C2	22µ 50V elect
C3	4µ7 63V elect
C4	2µ2 63V elect
C5	1µ 63V elect
C6	4µ7 63V elect
C7	27p ceramic plate
C8	10µ 50V elect

Semiconductors
| IC1 | NE5534A |
| IC2 | LF351N |

Miscellaneous
JK1	standard jack socket
JK2	standard jack socket
	Two 8 pin d.i.l. i.c. holders, circuit board, case, etc.

Crystal Microphone Preamplifier

Although they were all the rage about twenty years or so ago, crystal microphones seem to have steadily fallen from favour over the intervening years. They have been ousted by dynamic and electret types. Cheap dynamic types now tend to be used where inexpensive crystal microphones might once have been used, while electret microphones are now used in place of the higher quality crystal types. Probably the main cause of this decline is the fact that crystal microphones have output characteristics that are fine for use with valve circuits, but which are less well suited to bipolar transistor circuits. As valves were used less and less in audio equipment, crystal microphones became less and less popular.

Crystal microphones are still available today, mainly in the form of inexpensive lapel microphones. Also, with large numbers of them having been sold over many years, there must still be large numbers of them in circulation. Where a rugged and moderately good quality microphone is required they still represent a good choice. Although they are not ideally suited to use with old style bipolar transistor circuits, they actually operate well with modern semiconductor components. In particular, they work well with f.e.t.s and f.e.t. input operational amplifiers.

The output level from crystal microphones is quite high (by microphone standards anyway). An output of around 10 millivolts r.m.s. is generally produced by crystal lapel microphones, with the higher quality "stick" types usually producing a slightly lower output level. This is not quite as good as it might at first appear, because the output signal is at a very high impedance. I suppose that this is not strictly true, and it would be more accurate to say that a crystal microphone must feed into a very high load impedance.

A microphone of this type effectively consists of a low impedance signal source in series with a capacitor (Fig.1.8). The value of this capacitor varies substantially from one microphone to another, but it is never very large. It would

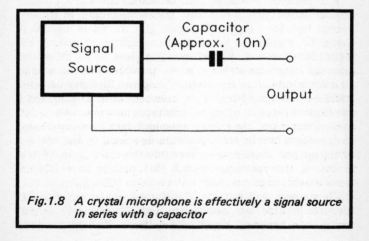

Fig.1.8 A crystal microphone is effectively a signal source in series with a capacitor

typically be around 10 nanofarads. This gives the microphone an output impedance that is almost totally dependent on frequency, and which halves with every doubling of frequency. The output impedance is quite low at the highest audio frequencies, but is one megohm or more at the low end of the audio range. The built-in capacitance and the input impedance of the preamplifier effectively form a single stage highpass filter. This makes it essential to have a high load impedance, as the microphone otherwise has a frequency response that rises at 6dB per octave over a large part of the audio range! An input impedance of about 1 megohm is usually sufficient to give good results, with a reasonably well extended low frequency response.

Figure 1.9 shows the circuit diagram for a crystal microphone preamplifier. This consists of a unity gain buffer stage at the input, a volume control style variable attenuator, and an inverting amplifier to provide the voltage gain. The specified values for R1 and R2 give an input impedance of 1.1 megohms, which should be satisfactory with all crystal microphones. However, these values can be raised if necessary, so as to provide a higher input impedance. For example, 3.9 megohm resistors could be used for a microphone that has a recommended load impedance of 2 megohms.

IC2 provides a voltage gain of 40dB (100 times), which should match practically any crystal microphone to any normal high level input. If higher gain should be needed it would be possible to boost the gain slightly by making R6 higher in value. As IC2 is operating close to its maximum practical closed loop gain it is not possible to obtain a large increase in gain from this stage. A negative feedback network could be introduced to IC1 in order to boost its gain, but I would warn against trying to produce a large increase in the gain of this stage. As it has a very high input impedance and its input and output are in-phase, more than a modest amount of voltage gain could easily cause instability. The output levels of crystal microphones are such that nothing more than a modest boost in gain is likely to be needed anyway.

Once again, construction of this unit is basically straightforward, but the high gain makes it mandatory to be careful about the component layout. As with the other microphone

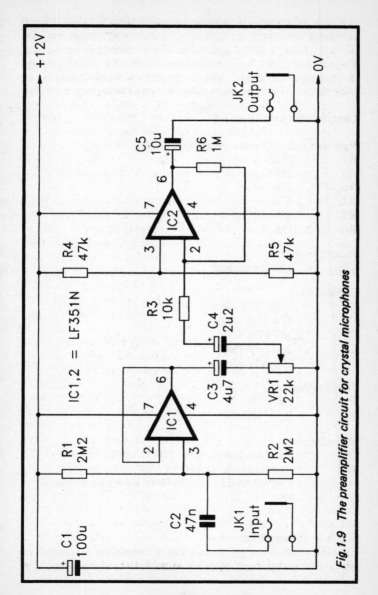

Fig.1.9 The preamplifier circuit for crystal microphones

27

preamplifiers, good screening is essential in order to avoid problems with pick up of mains "hum". Although the gain of this preamplifier is somewhat lower than that of the previous two circuits, it is probably more prone to stray pick-up in the input circuitry. This is due to its much higher input impedance, which renders fully effective screening essential.

Components for Figure 1.9

Resistors (all 0.25 watt 5% carbon film)
R1	2M2
R2	2M2
R3	10k
R4	47k
R5	47k
R6	1M

Potentiometer
VR1	22k log carbon

Capacitors
C1	100μ 25V elect
C2	47n polyester
C3	$4\mu7$ 63V elect
C4	$2\mu2$ 63V elect
C5	10μ 50V elect

Semiconductors
IC1	LF351N
IC2	LF351N

Miscellaneous
JK1	standard jack socket
JK2	standard jack socket
	Two 8 pin d.i.l. i.c. holders, case, circuit board, etc.

R.I.A.A. Preamplifier
Despite predictions by many that it would be a number of years before sales of compact disks overtook those of L.P.

gramophone records, it did not really happen that way. In fact L.P.s were soon in third place behind compact cassettes. Despite their fall in relative popularity, gramophone records are still popular in absolute terms. With large numbers of people having substantial record collections, and much of the programme material never likely to appear on compact disks, this medium will remain in use for many years to come.

The preamplifier requirements of a magnetic cartridge are slightly unusual in that they involve doctoring of the frequency response. This is not due to any innate problems with the frequency response of the recording and playback system. This gives what is essentially a flat response, apart from any slight irregularities caused by imperfections in the equipment used. The tailoring of the preamplifier's frequency response is needed in order to counteract the treble boost and bass cut that are purposely applied to the recorded signal.

The high frequency boost is a form of noise reduction, and one that is used in most recording systems, as well as many radio broadcasting systems. The idea is that by applying some treble boost during the recording process, it is possible to apply complementary treble cut during playback without compromising the performance of the system. The overall frequency response is flat, but the treble cut applied during playback helps to reduce "hiss" type noise generated within the recording system. The treble boost is called "pre-emphasis", and the treble cut is called "de-emphasis". The bass cut during the recording process is needed to avoid excessive groove modulation on strong low frequency signals. Again, by applying complementary response tailoring during playback a flat overall frequency response is obtained.

Figure 1.10 shows the ideal response for a magnetic cartridge which has standard R.I.A.A. equalisation. The response is rolled-off at 6dB per octave above 2120 hertz (i.e. the gain halves above this figure for each doubling of the input frequency). The gain is boosted by 6dB per octave at frequencies below 500 hertz. There is also a requirement for the response to be rolled-off below 20 hertz in order to avoid problems with the low frequency noise which tends to be generated by this recording medium. This roll-off would normally be provided by the coupling capacitors in the system anyway, and does not

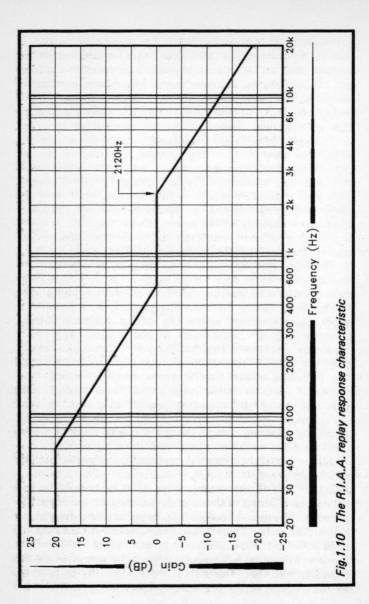

Fig. 1.10 The R.I.A.A. replay response characteristic

require any additional components.

In practice the ideal response can never be achieved, since the boost and cut can not be suddenly introduced at the full rate. With complex filters it would be possible to achieve something very close indeed to the required response, but practical R.I.A.A. equalisation circuits generally use simple filtering techniques. These introduce some slight errors in the response, but these should not be large enough to noticeably degrade performance.

An R.I.A.A. preamplifier circuit based on operational amplifiers is shown in Figure 1.11. As we shall see later, there is an alternative approach in the form of audio integrated circuits designed specifically for this application.

IC1 is a high quality audio operational amplifier which has suitably low noise and distortion figures for a hi-fi application such as this. It acts as an input stage which provides some of the circuit's voltage gain (just over 20dB of it). It also sets the input impedance at about 47k, which is the optimum figure for most magnetic cartridges. Note though, that some have a recommended load impedance of 100k, and would require R1 and R2 to be raised to 200k each for optimum performance.

Although the specified values for R1 and R2 would seem to give something less than optimum biasing, this is not really the case. Most operational amplifiers have non-symmetrical output stages which can provide output levels much closer to one supply rail than the other. In most cases this means that the output voltage can go within about one volt of the positive supply rail, but can not get within about two volts of the negative supply potential. Thus, a slightly higher bias level than the normal half supply level actually gives slightly improved results with these devices.

IC2 provides further voltage amplification, and also gives the required tailoring of the frequency response. Incidentally, the treble cut applied by IC2 helps to combat the noise produced by IC1. It is therefore better to have the equalisation at the output of the circuit rather than at the input. The equalisation relies on the fact that the impedance of a capacitor halves with each doubling of frequency. Therefore, if a capacitor is used in the negative feedback of an operational

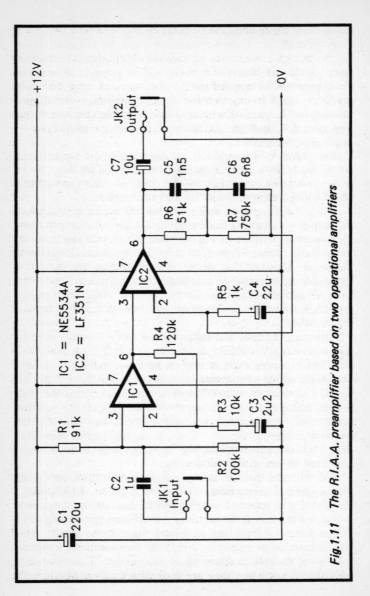

Fig.1.11 The R.I.A.A. preamplifier based on two operational amplifiers

IC1 = NE5534A
IC2 = LF351N

+12V
0V

JK2 Output

C7 10u
C5 1n5
C6 6n8
R6 51k
R7 750k

R5 1k
C4 22u

R4 120k

R1 91k

R3 10k
C3 2u2

C2 1u
JK1 Input
R2 100k

C1 220u

amplifier it can be made to give the required 6dB per octave roll-off rate.

In this case we do not require a straightforward 6dB per octave roll-off across the entire audio range. Instead, the filtering must be applied over two bands of frequencies. This is achieved by having two feedback capacitors, with each one connected in parallel with a resistor. These components are R6, R7, C5, and C6. At low frequencies the impedances of C5 and C6 are too high to have any effect on the gain of the circuit, and it is therefore set at roughly 800 times by the three resistors in the feedback circuit.

At frequencies of about 50 hertz or more the impedance of C6 becomes relatively low in comparison to that of R7, and it provides the required rolling off of the frequency response. However, at frequencies of around 500 hertz its value becomes low relative to that of R6, and it then provides little further rolling-off of the frequency response. At frequencies above 2 kilohertz or so C5 has an impedance which is low in relation to that of R6, and it therefore provides the required high frequency roll-off.

High frequency stability should not be a major problem with this preamplifier, since its high frequency gain is not very high, and the input and output of the circuit are out-of-phase. Low frequency stability is another matter. The gain of the amplifier is very high at low frequencies, being several thousand times at frequencies of around 20 to 50 hertz. This makes the circuit very vulnerable to pick-up of mains "hum" and other low frequency noise. The circuit in general, but the input wiring in particular, therefore needs to be scrupulously screened.

Another problem with this high gain at low frequencies is that of "hum" and feedback loops. These are caused by the small voltages that are generated across the earth wires due to their minute resistances. These voltages are insignificant if everything is earthed properly, but can (and probably will) cause problems if the earthing is not arranged sensibly. This is a potential problem with any high gain circuit, which includes the microphone preamplifiers described previously. There is no real problem when the preamplifiers are used in isolation; it is when they are used with a power amplifier that there are potential problems.

There are two basic approaches to successful earthing. These are called the "spider" and "bus-bar" earthing systems. In theory the spider earth is the simpler, but it can be difficult to implement properly in practice. It simply has everything earthed to a common point, as in the diagrammatic representation of Figure 1.12. The "bus-bar" earthing system is usually easier to implement in real-life, and this has a wire (or p.c.b. track) going to the earth points in their natural sequence. In other words, first the supply and the loudspeaker are earthed, then the output stage, followed by the driver stage, the pre-amplifier, and the input socket. This arrangement is shown in Figure 1.13, and it really just has things earthed in the same order that the earth connections normally appear on a circuit diagram. What must be avoided at all costs is having the input earthed somewhere between the loudspeaker/output stage and the supply.

This circuit should work well with most magnetic cartridges. If overloading should occur at high volume levels, make R5 a little higher in value. A value of 2k2 should be satisfactory. Conversely, if the output seems to be inadequate, make R5 lower in value. A 680R component should be satisfactory. It is perhaps worth mentioning that many magnetic cartridges

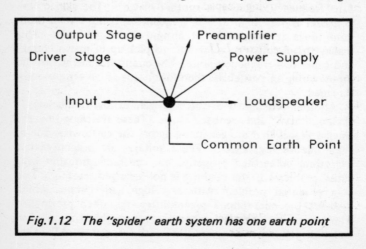

Fig.1.12   The "spider" earth system has one earth point

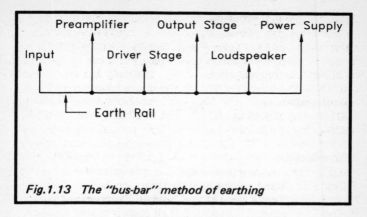

Fig.1.13 The "bus-bar" method of earthing

are at their best when loaded with a capacitance of a few hundred picofarads. This is substantially higher than the innate input capacitance of most R.I.A.A. preamplifiers, even when the capacitance of the screened cable is taken into account. Therefore, results might be improved somewhat by adding a capacitor of around 100p to 270p in value across the input of the preamplifier. Of course, the exact effect this will have depends on the particular cartridge used, but it might be worthwhile trying a capacitor of about 150p in value across the input.

Components for Figure 1.11

Resistors (all 0.25 watt 5% carbon film)

R1	91k
R2	100k
R3	10k
R4	120k
R5	1k
R6	51k
R7	750k

Capacitors

C1	220µ 25V elect
C2	1µ polyester

C3	2μ2 63V elect
C4	22μ 25V elect
C5	1n5 polyester (5% or better)
C6	6n8 polyester (5% or better)
C7	10μ 50V elect

Semiconductors

IC1	NE5534A
IC2	LF351N

Miscellaneous

JK1	standard jack socket
JK2	standard jack socket
	Two 8 pin d.i.l. i.c. holders, circuit board, case, etc.

Note that for stero operation two preamplifiers will be needed, one for each stereo channel. Therefore, two of each component will be required, apart from the case which must be large enough to accommodate two preamplifier boards.

Alternative R.I.A.A. Preamplifier
There are numerous audio preamplifier integrated circuits currently being manufactured, including some that are primarily designed for use in R.I.A.A. preamplifiers. The HA12017 is an example of such an integrated circuit. It has impressive performance figures with a typical total harmonic distortion figure of 0.002% (0.01% maximum), and a typical unweighted output noise voltage of 53 microvolts (90 microvolts maximum). This equates to a signal-to-noise ratio that would normally be between 80 and 100dB.

Figure 1.14 shows the internal arrangement used for this device, and it also shows the pin numbers. The encapsulation is an unusual one incidentally. It is basically an 8-pin s.i.l. (single in line) type, but with pin 2 omitted. If you do not wish to solder it direct to the circuit board, and you can not obtain an 8-pin s.i.l. socket, it will plug into one side of a 16-pin d.i.l. holder. It will also plug into a row of eight "Soldercon" pins.

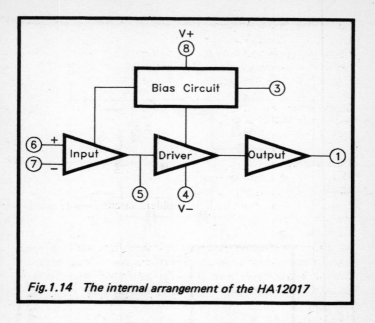

Fig.1.14 The internal arrangement of the HA12017

There is a differential amplifier at the input, and the device is basically a high gain operational amplifier optimised for audio applications. The differential input stage is followed by driver and output stages. The circuit includes a bias generator stage, but this does not include any input biasing components. It provides bias currents and voltages for later parts of the amplifier chain. This means that in a practical circuit the device is used much like an operational amplifier.

The circuit diagram for an R.I.A.A. preamplifier based on the HA12017 is shown in Figure 1.15. Although this device could probably be used successfully with a single supply rail, the manufacturers' data only seems to recommend dual supply operation. Therefore, unlike the other circuits in this book, this one operates from dual balanced 12-volt supplies. The recommended supply voltage is plus and minus 24 volts, but unless high output voltage swings are required it will work perfectly well from dual 12-volt supplies. Note that the absolute maximum supply voltage is plus and minus 26.5 volts,

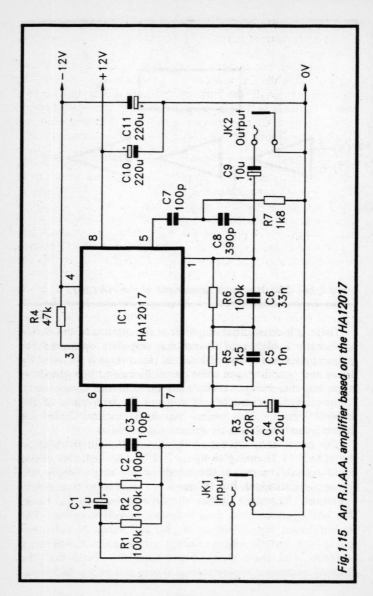

Fig. 1.15 An R.I.A.A. amplifier based on the HA12017

38

and that the minimum requirement is plus and minus 6 volts. The supply current is typically 4 milliamps, but can be up to 6 milliamps.

R2 biases the non-inverting input to the central 0 volt supply rail while C1 provides d.c. blocking at the input. The d.c. flow through the cartridge without C1 would be very small, but it is best to avoid any d.c. flow through the coil of the cartridge. C1 also provides protection if there should be a fault. R1 shunts the input impedance of the circuit to 50k. For an input impedance of 47k use a 91k component, or omit R1 altogether if an input impedance of 100k is required. C2 and C3 aid stability, and also provide the circuit with a more suitable input capacitance.

The negative feedback network has C5, R5, C6, and R6 as the R.I.A.A. equalisation network, and R3 as the other arm of the network. C4 provides d.c. blocking in the feedback network, and in theory this component is not required. However, with practical differential amplifiers there tend to be unwanted offset voltages. These are quite small, but are effectively multiplied by the d.c. voltage gain of the circuit. This can produce very large offsets at the output, and could prevent the circuit from operating at all. This is avoided by the inclusion of a d.c. blocking capacitor which gives the circuit a d.c. voltage gain of just one. This capacitor also helps to provide the required roll-off below 20 hertz. C7, C8, and R7 aid high frequency stability, and are what might be regarded as external compensation components.

Some audio preamplifier integrated circuits tend to be fussy about component layouts. However, with the HA12017 there is no major stability problem, and the component layout is not particularly critical. Bear in mind though, the potential problems of "hum" pick-up and loops that were mentioned previously. The gain of the circuit should be suitable for most magnetic cartridges, but the gain can be boosted somewhat, if necessary, by using a slightly lower value for R3.

Components for Figure 1.15

Resistors (all 0.25 watt 5% carbon film)
R1	100k
R2	100k
R3	220R
R4	47k
R5	7k5
R6	100k
R7	1k8

Capacitors
C1	1µ 63V elect
C2	100p polystyrene
C3	100p polystyrene
C4	220µ 25V elect
C5	10n polyester (5% or better)
C6	33n polyester (5% or better)
C7	100p ceramic plate
C8	390p ceramic plate
C9	10µ 50V elect
C10	220µ 25V elect
C11	220µ 25V elect

Semiconductor
IC1	HA12017

Miscellaneous
JK1	standard jack socket
JK2	standard jack socket
	8 pin s.i.l. i.c. holder (see text), circuit board, case, etc.

Note that for stereo operation two preamplifiers will be needed, one for each stereo channel. Therefore, two of each component will be required, apart from the case which must be large enough to accommodate two preamplifier boards. The HA12017 is available from RS outlets, including "Electromail".

Ceramic Cartridge Preamplifier

Crystal and ceramic cartridges were once popular for use in low cost record playing equipment, but in recent years they seem to have been replaced to some extent by low cost magnetic cartridges. They are still far from obsolete though, and there must be very large numbers still in use. They are certainly still used in some new equipment. Incidentally, the only difference between crystal and ceramic cartridges is that one is based on a natural crystal, whereas a piece of man-made ceramic material forms the basis for the other.

They operate on the same principle and have similar output characteristics. They rely on the Piezo effect. This is where a piece of suitable crystal/ceramic material has two electrodes on opposite surfaces. If the unit is twisted or bent, a charge is produced across the two electrodes. The greater the twisting or bending force, the higher the charge voltage. Movement in one direction produces a positive charge — movement in the opposite direction generates a negative charge. Obviously this effect can be used to convert groove modulations of a record into equivalent electrical signals.

Crystal and ceramic cartridges operate on the same principle as crystal microphones, and have similar output characteristics. This means that they must feed into a high load impedance if they are to achieve a good bass response. The output level is generally much higher than that from a crystal microphone, and is usually somewhere between 100 millivolts r.m.s. and 1 volt r.m.s. at high modulation levels. This means that in order to drive most high level inputs some high impedance buffering is needed, but little voltage amplification is required.

A single stage amplifier such as the one shown in the circuit diagram of Figure 1.16 should be satisfactory. This is basically just an operational amplifier used in the non-inverting mode. R1 and R2 set the input impedance at about 1.1 megohms. Their value can obviously be changed in order to give a different input impedance if your cartridge has a recommended load impedance that greatly differs from this figure of 1.1 megohms. R3 and R4 set the voltage gain at between five and six times, which should be adequate for all but the lowest output pickups. If necessary, the gain can be boosted by making R3 a

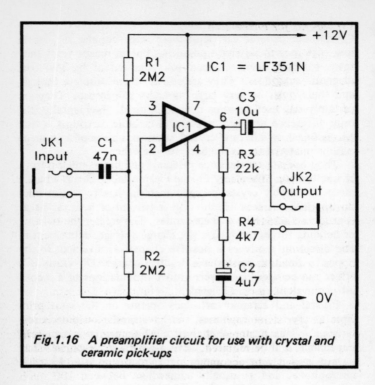

Fig.1.16 A preamplifier circuit for use with crystal and ceramic pick-ups

little higher in value. It is more likely that a high output pick-up will overload the circuit, in which case R3 should be made lower in value.

This circuit is very simple, and does not have very high voltage gain. This makes the component layout something less than critical. On the other hand, bear in mind that the circuit has a high input impedance, and that the input and output are in-phase. Reasonable care needs to be taken with the component layout in order to avoid problems with mild instability. The high input impedance of the circuit also makes good screening important, as the circuit is vulnerable to stray pick-up of mains "hum", etc.

Components for Figure 1.16

Resistors (all 0.25 watt 5% carbon film)
R1   2M2
R2   2M2
R3   22k
R4   4k7

Capacitors
C1   47n polyester
C2   4µ7 63V elect
C3   10µ 50V elect

Semiconductor
IC1   LF351N

Miscellaneous
JK1   standard jack socket
JK2   standard jack socket
            8 pin d.i.l. i.c. holder, circuit board, case, etc.

Note that for stereo operation two preamplifiers will be needed, one for each stereo channel. Therefore, two of each
components will be required, apart from the case which must
be large enough to accommodate two preamplifier boards.

Tape Preamplifier

Do-it-yourself tape recorders are a difficult prospect due to
the difficulty of getting everything set up properly. Quite
minor errors in a.c. bias levels and other factors can seriously
degrade performance. These problems are not insurmount-
able, but make such a project unsuitable for anyone who does
not possess a reasonable amount of audio test equipment, and
a good knowledge of how to use it. The same is not true of a
tape replay system. This avoids the complications associated
with bias levels, etc., of a recording system, and requires only
some fairly basic circuitry.

Cassette mechanisms complete with stereo heads are available from time to time on the surplus market at quite low

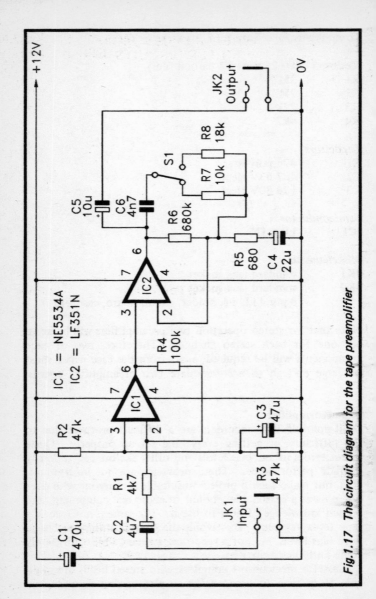

Fig.1.17 The circuit diagram for the tape preamplifier

44

prices. One of these plus a simple tape preamplifier can make a cheap but good cassette player. You might even be able to salvage a suitable mechanism and heads from a defunct cassette recorder or deck. Most cassette mechanisms have two heads, which are the erase head and a combined record/replay type. In this application two heads are not better than one. The erase head is not needed, and can be removed or just ignored. If you are in doubt as to which head is which, things are normally arranged so that the tape passes the erase head first (so that anything already recorded on the tape is erased before new material is placed on the tape). You can always try the two heads to determine which one gives the best results. The output quality of an erase head is such that you will be in no doubt as to which head is which after this "acid" test!

Figure 1.17 shows the circuit diagram for a simple cassette tape preamplifier. Like an R.I.A.A. preamplifier, a tape type must provide both a large amount of voltage amplification and some equalisation. The output from a tape head is usually well under one millivolt r.m.s., and the source impedance is quite low. In fact the output characteristics of a tape head are broadly similar to those of a low impedance dynamic microphone.

The equalisation is required due to the fact that the output from a tape head rises at 6dB per octave. Therefore, in order to produce a flat frequency response the playback preamplifier must provide a 6dB per octave roll-off. In practice matters are not quite as simple as this. Treble boost (pre-emphasis) is applied during the recording process as part of a simple noise reducing process. On the face of it, this makes it necessary to apply more treble cut in order to produce a flat overall frequency response.

In reality the amount of treble cut required is far less than one would expect. This is due to the imperfect performance of the tape heads which give lower than optimum output levels at high frequencies. In fact they give far lower output levels at treble frequencies than would be expected. Thus the roll-off only needs to be applied over the low and middle frequency ranges, and must flatten out at high frequencies.

The input stage is an inverting mode circuit having a voltage of a little over 26dB (twenty times), and an input impedance of about 4k7. A low noise operational amplifier is used for IC1 in order to produce a good signal-to-noise ratio despite the high sensitivity of the circuit. In fact the noise is likely to be predominantly tape "hiss" rather than noise from the preamplifier itself. If you are not intent on having the ultimate in noise performance it is quite acceptable to use a μA741C, LF351N, etc., for IC1.

IC2 is a non-inverting amplifier, and it is this stage that provides the equalisation. C6 provides the 6dB per octave roll-off while either R7 or R8 limits the frequency range over which the roll-off is applied. R8 is switched into circuit in order to give the standard tape preamplifier equalisation characteristic.

With R7 switched into circuit the attenuation is applied over a wider frequency range, and at high frequencies there is slightly more attenuation. This setting is used when playing cassettes that have been encoded using the Dolby B system. This does not constitute proper Dolby B decoding, which requires dynamic filtering. In other words, the degree of filtering must be continuously altered to suit the input level (the higher the input level the more severe the top-cut filtering). This extra filtering helps to give a flatter overall frequency response, and a small amount of noise reduction (about 5dB).

At one time some form of noise reduction was essential in order to obtain reasonable results from cassette tape equipment. Without noise reduction the signal-to-noise ratio was generally only about 40dB to 50dB, with Dolby B noise reduction increasing the noise performance by about 10dB. With modern circuits, tape heads, and tapes, it is possible to obtain quite usable results without noise reduction circuits (as many "Walkman" units demonstrate). In fact modern tape equipment which does not use any noise reduction can easily out-perform older equipment that uses the Dolby B system.

Construction of this amplifier is not critical since the input and output are out-of-phase, and the input impedance is not very high. On the other hand, the high gain at low frequencies does mean that the circuit is very vulnerable to stray pick-up of mains "hum" and other low frequency noise. This includes noise from the motor in the cassette deck. It is also vulnerable to earth and "hum" loops. Therefore, take due care with screening, the earthing, and the decoupling of the supply if a common supply is used for the preamplifier and the cassette deck.

Components for Figure F1.17

Resistors (all 0.25 watt 5% carbon film)

R1	4k7
R2	47k
R3	47k
R4	100k
R5	680R
R6	680k
R7	10k
R8	18k

Capacitors

C1	470μ 25V elect
C2	4μ7 63V elect
C3	47μ 25V elect
C4	22μ 25V elect
C5	10μ 50V elect
C6	4n7 polyester (5% or better)

Semiconductors

IC1	NE5534A
IC2	LF351N

Miscellaneous

JK1	standard jack socket
JK2	standard jack socket
	Two 8 pin d.i.l. i.c. holders, circuit board, case, etc.

Note that for stereo operation two preamplifiers will be needed, one for each stereo channel. Therefore, two of each component will be required, apart from the case which must be large enough to accommodate two preamplifier boards.

Finally

This covers preamplifiers for the popular signal sources. For any unusual requirements it would probably be possible to adapt one of the circuits described here to suit your requirements. It should perhaps be pointed out that for high level signal sources such as compact disc players, cassette units, and radio tuners it is not normally necessary to use a preamplifier. These have low output impedances and quite high signal levels of about one volt r.m.s., which enables them to drive most power amplifiers, etc., without any assistance. Where there is a problem with a slightly inadequate output level and (or) a high output impedance, a simple low voltage gain stage will usually suffice. The preamplifier circuit for ceramic and crystal pick-ups is quite good for this type of thing.

Chapter 2

FILTERS, TONE CONTROLS, MIXERS, ETC.

In this second chapter we will mainly be concerned with filter circuits, such as tone controls, and scratch and rumble filters. Some other audio preamplifier related topics are also considered, such as audio level limiting, and audio mixing.

Mono to Stereo
One of the more commonly asked questions when audio power amplifier designs are published is "how do I produce a stereo version of the amplifier"? The simple answer is that you build two of them, one for each stereo channel. I suppose that in truth this is a slight over-simplification, since the two power amplifier modules are normally united via a common volume control and balance control.

The most simple form of volume and balance control is the type which uses a dual concentric potentiometer. This is basically just a dual gang potentiometer with one section used as the volume control for the left channel, and the other connected as the volume control for the right hand channel. The two gangs are controlled via separate but concentric control knobs which are easily adjusted in unison. However, there is no difficulty in holding one knob still while moving the other, so that the two volume levels can be set for an accurate balance. This method is quite a good one, but it seems to be far more common on stereo cassette decks than on stereo power amplifiers. For the home constructor it has the advantage of being simple and straightforward, but the disadvantage that suitable components tend to be very difficult to obtain.

Most stereo power amplifiers have a common volume control which uses an ordinary twin gang potentiometer. Channel balancing is effected by a separate control, which in most cases is a single gang potentiometer. Figure 2.1 shows the circuit diagram for a volume and balance control of this type. VR1a and VR1b are the standard stereo volume control, with one gang connected in each channel. The two output signals are taken via series resistors R1 and R2, and there will be

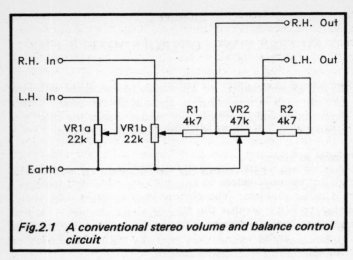

Fig.2.1 A conventional stereo volume and balance control circuit

small losses due to the voltage drops through these resistors. We are assuming here that the circuit feeds into a reasonably high load impedance of several kilohms or more. If the circuit feeds into a lower impedance, it will only work well if a buffer amplifier is used to reduce the loading on the output. We are also assuming here that VR2 is set at a roughly mid-setting. It then introduces relatively small signal losses due to the potential divider action with R1 and R2.

Moving the wiper of VR2 well towards the left end of its track produces large losses through R1 due to the low resistance through VR2 to earth. Taking the wiper fully to the left hand end of the track actually short circuits the output from R1 to earth, and cuts off the signal completely. It has the opposite effect on the signal through R2, which is connected to earth through the full resistance of VR2, causing minimal losses. Taking the wiper of VR2 to the other end of its track produces minimal losses through R1, but produces large losses through R2. Again, taking the wiper right to the end of the track cuts off the signal completely. However, it is the left hand signal that is cut off this time.

Therefore, by adjusting VR2 it is possible to have the left hand signal only, the right hand signal only, or a mixture of the two at any desired relative levels. This enables the correct channel balance to be obtained even if there are factors that cause a strong innate imbalance in the system. In practice quite large channel imbalances are not uncommon. Remember that even sitting a bit closer to one loudspeaker than to the other can severely upset the perceived balance of the system.

Obviously construction of a volume and balance control circuit should give no major problems. The circuit can easily be hard-wired, but try to keep the wiring as short as possible so that stray pick-up is kept to a low level. Normally the volume and balance controls are connected at the inputs of the power amplifiers. As the signal levels here tend to be quite high but the impedances do not, stray pick-up is not likely to be a major problem. You obviously need to take care when wiring up VR2, so that the balance control operates in the logical manner (clockwise rotation boosts the right hand channel — counter-clockwise rotation boosts the left hand channel).

Components for Figure 2.1

Resistors (all 0.25 watt 5% carbon film)
R1   4k7
R2   4k7

Potentiometers
VR1   22k log carbon dual gang
VR2   47k lin carbon

Miscellaneous
Two control knobs, wire, etc.

There is an alternative type of balance control which is sometimes used. Figure 2.2 shows the circuit for a control of this type. VR1 is a dual gang potentiometer connected in what is almost a conventional stereo volume control circuit. It differs from the normal volume control connection only in that the two gangs are connected in anti-phase. In other words, as one is adjusted for higher gain, the other is set for reduced gain. The potentiometer should be a linear type so that there

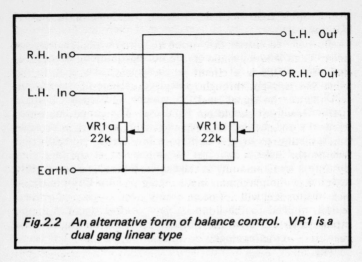

Fig.2.2 *An alternative form of balance control. VR1 is a dual gang linear type*

is a loss of 6dB through each channel at the central setting (a logarithmic type would give unequal losses at the central setting).

This type of balance control is in some ways a neater solution to the problem, but the loss of around 6dB through the circuit is somewhat higher than the typical signal loss through the type described previously. This is not a major signal loss though, and can usually be made up quite easily by boosting the gain of the preamplifier stage or stages. Alternatively the circuit can be followed by an amplifier having a voltage gain of about 6dB to compensate for the losses.

Audio Limiter

If a power amplifier should become seriously overloaded the result is severe clipping of the output signal. This has a disastrous affect on the output quality, with high levels of distortion being produced. The distortion products tend to be at high frequencies, and produce a pretty unpleasant sound. There is also a risk of damage to the tweeters in multi-way loudspeaker systems. The high frequency drivers are normally designed to handle only relatively modest power levels, but with a clipped signal they will receive much higher

52

power levels than normal. This can result in the voice-coil burning out.

One way to ensure that problems with overloading can not occur is to add an audio limiter at the input of the power amplifier. This is a circuit which normally lets the audio signal pass straight through to the power amplifier, but which will reduce the signal level if it exceeds a certain threshold figure. Ideally it should cut back the gain by amounts which keep the output level constant when an overload occurs. Practical limiter circuits permit some increase in the output level as the input is increased beyond the threshold level, but by only a small amount. If the threshold level is made slightly lower than the maximum input voltage required by the amplifier, overloading will not occur even if a grossly excessive input level is applied to the limiter. On the other hand, ordinary input signals can drive the amplifier to output powers that are very close to the maximum it can provide.

The block diagram of Figure 2.3 shows the arrangement used in a conventional audio limiter. The circuit is based on a voltage controlled attenuator (v.c.a.). This normally allows the input signal to pass through to the output with minimal losses. Its gain can be controlled by means of a d.c. voltage though, and by reducing this control voltage the losses through the circuit can be greatly increased.

In this case the control voltage is provided by a form of d.c. amplifier which normally has a high output voltage. This gives the required low losses through the v.c.a. under standby conditions. The input signal for the d.c. amplifier is derived from the output signal via a buffer stage, and a rectifier plus smoothing network. The buffer stage prevents the non-linear loading of the rectifier from producing distortion on the output signal. The rectifier and smoothing circuit produces a positive d.c. bias that is roughly proportional to the strength of the output signal. Small bias levels have no affect on the d.c. amplifier, but above a certain point only a minor increase in the input level produces a large reduction in the output voltage. Therefore, above a certain output level, the gain of the v.c.a. reduces substantially if the output level is increased. This gives a form of negative feedback action which tends to stabilise the output

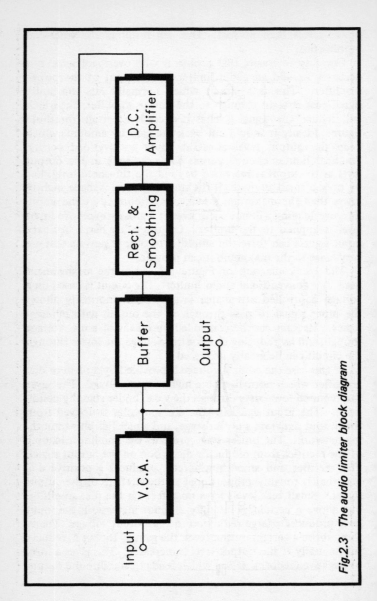

Fig.2.3 The audio limiter block diagram

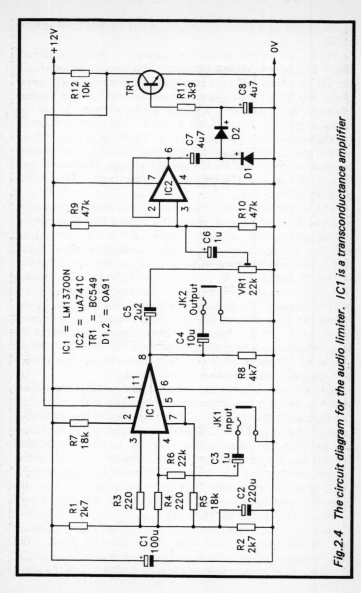

Fig.2.4 The circuit diagram for the audio limiter. IC1 is a transconductance amplifier

55

signal at the threshold level, provided the input level is high enough.

Figure 2.4 shows the circuit diagram for the audio limiter unit. This is based on an operational transconductance amplifier (IC1), which differs substantially from an ordinary operational amplifier. The main difference is that it is a current operated device, and not a voltage activated type. It has the usual differential inputs (pins 3 and 4), but these respond to the difference in the input currents. By using a series resistor at an input, the input current flow through the resistor becomes proportional to the applied voltage, effectively converting the input to a voltage operated type. This is the purpose of R6.

The output from the device is a current rather than a voltage, but by adding a load resistor the current flow is converted into a proportional output voltage. R5 is the output load resistor. Another respect in which a transconductance amplifier is radically different to an ordinary operational amplifier is that it has a control current input (pin 1). The output current is a function of the differential input current and this control current. In practice this means that the gain of the device can be controlled via the control current, and is proportional to it. In this case the control current is provided by R12, which also acts as the load resistor for TR1. By switching on TR1 some or all of the control current can be diverted, and the gain of IC1 can be greatly reduced.

R1, R2, and C2 provide a centre tap on the supply lines which is used for bias purposes. R7 provides a bias current to the linearising diodes in IC1. This helps to give low distortion at high input signal levels. The output impedance of the transconductance amplifier is quite high, but the LM13700N used for IC1 has a built-in output buffer amplifier. R8 acts as the output load resistor for this stage. There is no negative feedback network incidentally. Transconductance amplifiers are normally used open loop (as in this case), or with only a very small amount of negative feedback.

Some of the output signal is coupled to buffer amplifier IC2 via variable attenuator VR1. From here the signal is fed to a conventional rectifier and smoothing circuit based on D1 and D2. Due to the threshold voltage of TR1, and the small

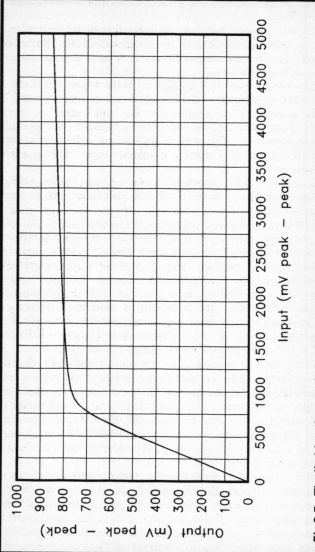

Fig.2.5 The limiting characteristic of the prototype (with VR1 set for zero attenuation)

voltage drops through the diodes, an output level of around 800 millivolts peak to peak is needed before TR1 will start to switch on. However, due to the low value of R11, an output voltage only slightly higher than this will cause TR1 to be biased virtually into saturation, giving around 90dB of attenuation through the v.c.a.

This well defined threshold point helps to give the circuit a very good limiting characteristic, rather than simply having it apply dynamic compression across a wide range of input levels. Figure 2.5 shows the limiting characteristic for the prototype circuit. This is with VR1 set for zero attenuation. If VR1 is backed-off slightly, a higher output level is needed in order to bring TR1 into conduction. VR1 can therefore be used to raise the limiting threshold level to any desired voltage (within reason) above the basic 800 millivolts peak to peak threshold level.

I suppose that strictly speaking IC1 does not act as a voltage controlled attenuator. It is really a sort of buffer amplifier, but as its voltage gain is never more than about unity, and can be substantially less than unity, it provides a form of variable attenuator action. I suppose that it is not strictly a voltage controlled circuit either, as it is a bias current that controls its gain. However, this is largely of academic importance.

Construction of this project is very straightforward. The component layout is not critical because the gain of the circuit is only about unity or less, and the input impedance is not very high at around 22k. Instability and stray pick-up are not likely to be problems. One point worth mentioning is that D1 and D2 are germanium diodes, and not the more familiar silicon type. This means that they are vulnerable to heat damage, and due care should therefore be exercised when soldering them into circuit. It should not be necessary to use a heat-shunt provided the soldered joints are completed reasonably swiftly.

The voltage gain of the circuit is approximately unity up to the limiting threshold. If desired, the voltage gain can be boosted by making R6 lower in value, but this will reduce the input impedance of the circuit. The input impedance is roughly equal to the value of R6. If reduced gain is needed, simply make R6 higher in value (which will boost the input impedance). VR1 should be backed-off as far as possible without the amplifier becoming overloaded on excessive input levels. Back it off too far and the unit will not prevent overloading. Back it off too little and the power amplifier will never be driven at something approaching maximum output power. A little experimentation should soon locate a suitable setting. Try to avoid having the limiter almost continuously driven beyond its threshold level. This would result in significant compression of the dynamic levels in the programme material.

Although IC1 is shown as an LM13700N in the components list, the LM13600N is virtually identical and is also suitable. These days most electronic component retailers seem to supply the LM13700N though.

Components for Figure 2.4

Resistors (all 0.25 watt 5% carbon film)

R1	2k7
R2	2k7
R3	220R
R4	220R
R5	18k
R6	22k
R7	18k
R8	4k7
R9	47k
R10	47k
R11	3k9
R12	10k

Potentiometer

VR1	22k sub-min preset

Capacitors

C1	100μ 25V elect
C2	220μ 25V elect
C3	1μ 63V elect
C4	10μ 50V elect
C5	2μ2 63V elect

C6	1µ 63V elect
C7	4µ7 63V elect
C8	4µ7 63V elect

Semiconductors

IC1	LM13700N or LM13600N
IC2	µA741C
TR1	BC549
D1	OA91
D2	OA91

Miscellaneous

JK1	standard jack socket
JK2	standard jack socket
	16 pin d.i.l. i.c. holder, 8 pin d.i.l. i.c.
	holder, case, circuit board, etc.

For stereo operation two sets of components are required, but obviously only one case of adequate size to accommodate everything is needed. Note that LM13700N actually contains two transconductance amplifiers and output buffer stages, and that it is possible to use one section in each stereo channel. This list gives connection details for the second section of the device. The supply terminals (pins 6 and 11) are common to both sections incidentally.

Function	*Section 1* *Pin No.*	*Section 2* *Pin No.*
Control Input	1	16
Diode Bias	2	15
+ input	3	14
− input	4	13
Amplifier Output	5	12
Buffer Input	7	10
Buffer Output	8	9

Scratch and Rumble

The quaintly named scratch and rumble filters are mainly designed for use in conjunction with record playing equipment.

Using good quality equipment and modern records there should actually be no need for either type of filtering. The background noise level should be low, with no "snap", "crackle", and "pop", or low frequency "clunks" and "rumbles". In the real world you will often be playing one of your favourite records from many years ago on something less than "state of the art" equipment.

Even well cared-for records tend to suffer from the effects of mild scratches and dust particles in the grooves over a period of time. The "hiss" level can also be quite high on older recordings, which were in many cases made from master recordings which had poor signal-to-noise ratios by modern standards. The low frequency noises can simply be due to inadequacies in the mechanism of the record deck. They can also be produced by warps and other mechanical problems with the record itself.

A scratch filter can be used to combat the high frequency noises, which includes both the "crackle" produced by small scratches and groove contamination, and ordinary "hiss" type noise. Opinions vary when it comes to choosing the best cut-off frequency and attenuation rate for this type of filter. It has to be a compromise between a low enough frequency to give good noise reduction, and a high enough frequency to prevent the audio quality from being degraded too far. Similarly, the roll-off rate needs to be high enough to give good noise reduction, but it should not be so fast as to make the filtering too obvious. Using so called "brick wall" filtering it is possible to get some very impressive levels of "crackle" reduction, but to my ears at any rate, this type of scratch filtering sounds pretty terrible. There is a similar problem with the rumble filtering, where it would be possible to get some impressive results by completely eliminating all the bass signals!

The scratch and rumble filters featured here both have an 18dB per octave roll-off rate. This is high enough to give a good degree of noise reduction, but it does not make the addition of the filtering over-obvious. The cut-off frequency of the scratch filter is at about 7kHz. This obviously trims a fair amount off the upper part of the audio range, but it leaves a sufficient high frequency content for subjectively good results. Setting the cut-off frequency any higher is likely to give too little "crackle" reduction to make the addition of the filtering worthwhile. The rumble filter has a cut-off frequency of about 100Hz, which gives significant trimming of the bass frequency content. It retains a reasonable degree of fidelity though, and provides quite high attenuation of very low frequency and sub-audio noise.

Sub-audio noise may not seem to be a problem, as it is clearly inaudible. However, strong very low frequency signals, such as those produced by many warped records, can have audible effects. The main problem is that of the power amplifier's biasing and the loudspeaker cone effectively being varied from their normal central settings. This can cause clipping and severe distortion on one set of half cycles on strong signals.

Figure 2.6 shows the approximate frequency response of the prototype scratch and rumble filters. As will be explained more fully later on, you can easily alter the cut-off frequencies to suit individual requirements.

The Circuits

Taking the scratch filter circuit first (Fig.2.7), this is a conventional third order active circuit. Although it might seem that a three-stage passive C — R filter would have the desired effect, the performance of such a filter tends to be rather poor in a practical situation. One problem with passive filters is that they are dependent on being fed from a low source impedance, and feeding into a high load impedance. This makes it essential to have input and output buffer stages in order to obtain reliable and predictable results. In this case IC1 is the input buffer and IC2 acts as the buffer at the output of the circuit.

Active filtering goes beyond this simple buffering though, and positive feedback is used to enhance performance. In this circuit the feedback consists of having the bottom end of C3 connected to the output of IC2 instead of going to earth. If we ignore this fact for the moment, the circuit is just a three-stage passive affair. The first stage is formed by R3 and C2, while the next two stages are comprised of R4 and C3, and R5 plus C4.

62

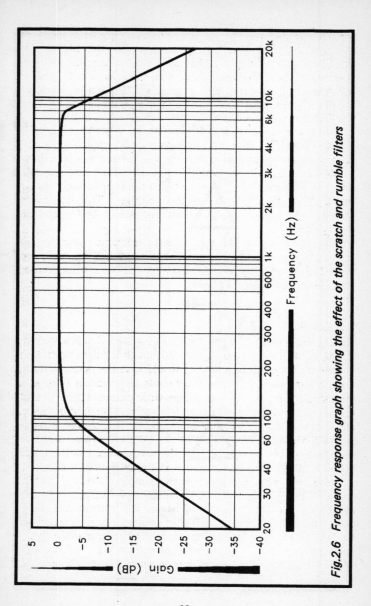

Fig.2.6 Frequency response graph showing the effect of the scratch and rumble filters

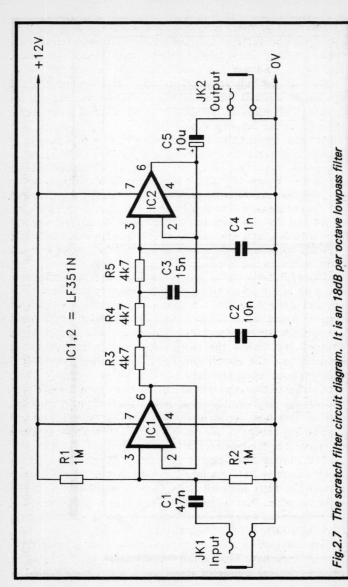

Fig.2.7 The scratch filter circuit diagram. It is an 18dB per octave lowpass filter

64

The main problem with a passive filter is that it tends to introduce the filtering quite gradually, with the full attenuation rate only being achieved well past the break frequency. The use of feedback can provide a much more abrupt introduction of the full attenuation rate. This avoids having a significant amount of attenuation well below the cut-off frequency in order to obtain the required amount of attenuation above the cut-off point.

At pass frequencies C3 has no effect. Any change in voltage at one end of the component is matched by an identical change at the other, giving no change in the charge voltage across C3. Below the cut-off frequency the situation is different, because the filtering provided by R5 and C4 means that the output signal will be smaller than the signal at the junction of R4 and R5. C3 then starts to provide filtering in conjunction with R4, and due to the relatively high value of C3, it provides quite strong filtering. This gives the required abrupt introduction of the filtering.

The explanation given above is a slight over-simplification, and with active filters such as this the circuit values have to be selected quite carefully. An error in one direction and the filtering is not much different to a passive design. An error in the opposite direction and the response can have a pronounced "hump" just below the cut-off frequency. In fact, in an extreme case the circuit can "ring", or actually break into oscillation at approximately the cut-off frequency. In an application of this type it is usually best to err on the safe side, and have a response that is completely free from resonances, even if this does result in the attenuation being introduced slightly less abruptly. As can be seen from the response curve of Figure 2.6, these filters are "hump" free.

The rumble filter circuit appears in Figure 2.8. This is much the same as the scratch filter, but resistors and capacitors in the filter network have been swopped over so that a highpass rather than a lowpass filter action is obtained. Also, the component values have obviously been changed to suit the required 100Hz cut-off frequency.

Construction of these circuits should present no real problems as they have only about unity voltage gain. Therefore, there is no real danger of instability. The circuit should be

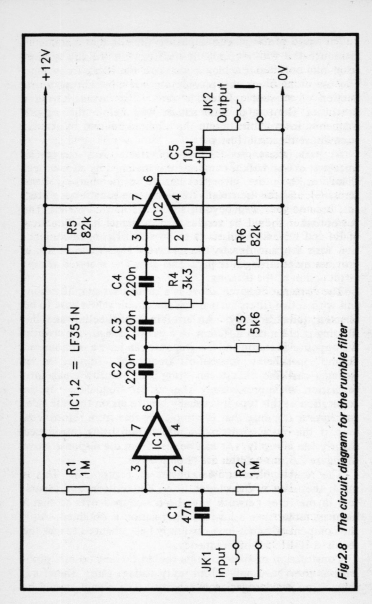

Fig.2.8 The circuit diagram for the rumble filter

added ahead of the power amplifier (not ahead of a preamplifier), where it will handle quite high signal levels. Stray pickup should not therefore be a major problem either.

When using filters of this type you should bear in mind that they are just simple filters, and that they can not work miracles! The scratch filter should be very effective against high frequency "hiss", and "clicks" produced by minor scratches and small dust particles. It can not combat large scratches as these produce signals over a wide range of frequencies, going well down into the audio range. A proper noise blanker is the only effective way of combatting severe scratches, and this is a relatively complex piece of equipment. It certainly goes well beyond the scope of this book. The rumble filter should be very effective against low frequency audio and sub-audio noise. It can not be expected to combat the noise from some very cheap record decks which is predominantly at relatively high frequencies.

Components for Figure 2.7

Resistors (all 0.25 watt 5% carbon film)

R1	1M
R2	1M
R3	4k7
R4	4k7
R5	4k7

Capacitors

C1	47n polyester
C2	10n polyester 5% or better
C3	15n polyester 5% or better
C4	1n polyester 5% or better
C5	10μ 50V elect

Semiconductors

IC1	LF351N
IC2	LF351N

Miscellaneous

JK1	standard jack socket

JK2   standard jack socket
Case, circuit board, two 8 pin d.i.l. i.c. holders, wire, solder, etc.

Note that for stereo operation two sets of components are required, but obviously only one case of adequate dimensions to accommodate both circuit boards is needed.

Components for Figure 2.8

Resistors (all 0.25 watt 5% carbon film)
R1	1M
R2	1M
R3	5k6
R4	3k3
R5	82k
R6	82k

Capacitors
C1	47n polyester
C2	220n polyester 5% or better
C3	220n polyester 5% or better
C4	220n polyester 5% or better
C5	10μ 50V elect

Semiconductors
IC1	LF351N
IC2	LF351N

Miscellaneous
JK1	standard jack socket
JK2	standard jack socket

Case, circuit board, two 8 pin d.i.l. i.c. holders, wire, solder, etc.

Note that for stereo operation two sets of components are required, but obviously only one case of adequate dimensions to accommodate both circuit boards is needed.

Switching

Neither the scratch or the rumble filters will be needed all the time, and some means of switching out the filtering will therefore be needed. The most simple method is to use an s.p.s.t. switch connected as shown in Figure 2.9. This shows the

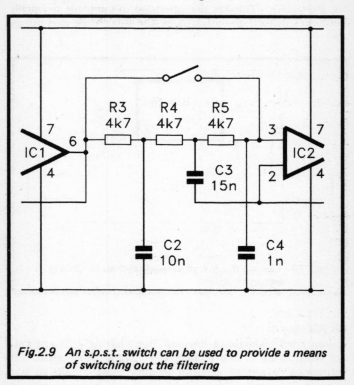

Fig.2.9 An s.p.s.t. switch can be used to provide a means of switching out the filtering

switch added to the scratch filter, but the same method of connection will work with the rumble filter (i.e. add the switch between IC1 pin 6 and IC2 pin 3). The additional switch leaves the circuit to function normally when left in the open position. When it is closed it bypasses the filter components and removes the filtering. This leaves some frequency dependant loading on the buffer amplifiers, but their low output impedances should prevent this from having any unwanted effects.

The alternative, and slightly better approach, is to use a d.p.d.t. switch to bypass the entire filter circuit when it is not required. Figure 2.10 shows the correct method of connection for the switch. This has the advantage of removing any slight noise and distortion generated by the filter when it is not in use.

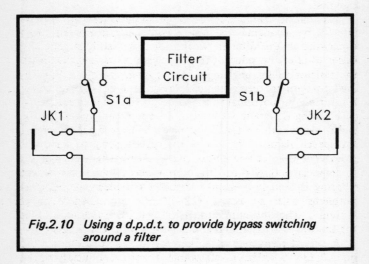

Fig.2.10   Using a d.p.d.t. to provide bypass switching around a filter

PA Filtering

If you need highpass or lowpass filters having different cut-off frequencies to the scratch and rumble filter circuits, it will probably not be difficult to alter these circuits to suit your requirements. You might require a minor change in frequency simply because you would prefer (say) a scratch filter with a somewhat lower cut-off frequency to combat more severe scratches. On the other hand, you might require a large change in order to suit a totally different application. Both are easily accommodated.

The cut-off frequency of the scratch filter can be altered by changing the values of the filter resistors and (or) capacitors.

In practice it is generally easier to change the value of the three resistors. The cut-off frequency is inversely proportional to the value of these resistors. In other words, doubling their value halves the cut-off frequency — halving their value doubles the cut-off frequency. A little mental arithmetic should produce a suitable value for an alternative cut-off frequency. It may be possible to "tweak" one or more of the filter capacitor values to suit your requirements, but this is by no means essential.

The cut-off frequency of the rumble filter can also be altered by changing the values of the resistors and (or) capacitors in the filter network. In this case it is generally easier to alter the value of the three capacitors, and then leave the resistor values unchanged, apart from any slight "tweaking" to optimise performance. Again, the cut-off frequency is inversely proportional to the values of the filter components.

Filtering is sometimes used in PA equipment to restrict the audio bandwidth to the frequencies that are most important for speech signals. This helps the speech signal to stand out from what will often be quite a hub-bub of background sounds. In some cases only topcut filtering is used. When only topcut filtering is used it is mainly included as a means of reducing problems with acoustic feedback and the dreaded "howl around". The optimum cut-off frequencies are about 2.5kHz for the lowpass filter, and about 300Hz for the highpass filter.

A cut-off frequency of 2.5kHz is not quite one-third of the scratch filter's 7kHz cut-off point. Therefore, multiplying the 4k7 filter resistor value by a little under three will give a suitable resistor value. 4k7 multiplied by three equals 14.1k, and the next value down from this in the E12 series of values is 12k, which should give something very close to the required cut-off frequency.

The rumble filter has a cut-off frequency of 100Hz, but we require a figure some three times higher. The filter capacitors therefore need to be one-third of the original value (which was 220n). 220n divided by three equals 73.33n, and the nearest E12 value to this is 68n.

Figures 2.11 and 2.12 are respectively for lowpass and highpass filters for PA applications. These follow the design method described above, and as can be seen from the frequency

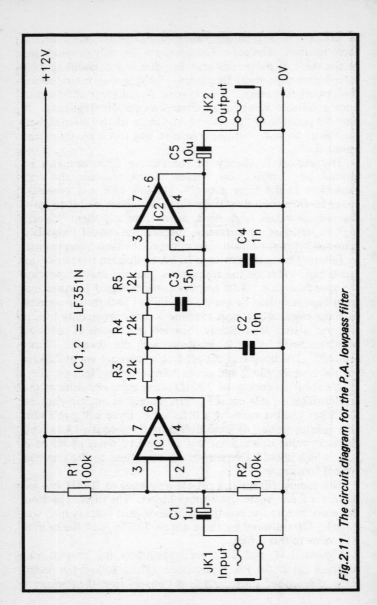

Fig.2.11   The circuit diagram for the P.A. lowpass filter

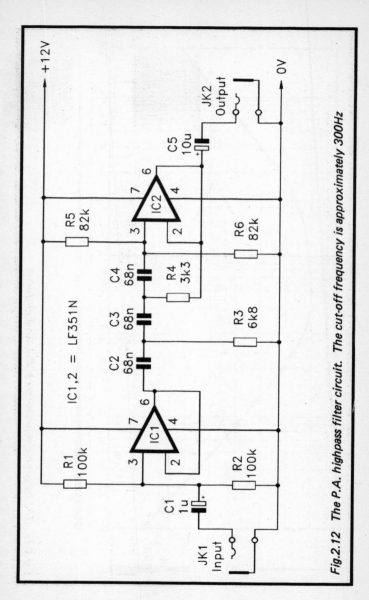

Fig.2.12   The P.A. highpass filter circuit.   The cut-off frequency is approximately 300Hz

73

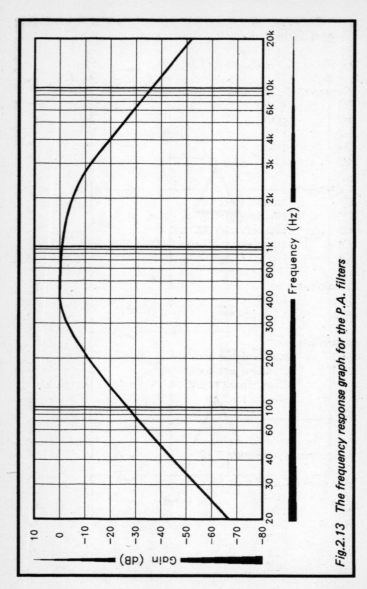

Fig.2.13 The frequency response graph for the P.A. filters

response graph of Figure 2.13, these changes in value have very much the desired effect.

Components for Figure 2.11

Resistors (all 0.25 watt 5% carbon film)
R1	100k
R2	100k
R3	12k
R4	12k
R5	12k

Capacitors
C1	1μ 63V elect
C2	10n polyester 5% or better
C3	15n polyester 5% or better
C4	1n polyester 5% or better
C5	10μ 50V elect

Semiconductors
| IC1 | LF351N |
| IC2 | LF351N |

Miscellaneous
JK1	standard jack socket
JK2	standard jack socket
	Case, circuit board, two 8 pin d.i.l. i.c. holders, wire, solder, etc.

Components for Figure 2.12

Resistors (all 0.25 watt 5% carbon film)
R1	100k
R2	100k
R3	6k8
R4	3k3
R5	82k
R6	82k

Capacitors

C1	1µ 63V elect
C2	68n polyester 5% or better
C3	68n polyester 5% or better
C4	68n polyester 5% or better
C5	10µ 50V elect

Semiconductors

IC1	LF351N
IC2	LF351N

Miscellaneous

JK1	standard jack socket
JK2	standard jack socket
	Case, circuit board, two 8 pin d.i.l. i.c. holders, wire, solder, etc.

Tone Controls

Tone controls seem to be a feature of most audio amplifiers, and these are usually in the form of bass and treble controls capable of providing about 12dB or so of boost or cut over their respective frequency bands. Although they are very simple circuits, many tone control designs seem to have rather unusual control characteristics if you make some careful checks on them! The problem is usually a lack of symmetry in the boost/cut characteristic. This is not really a fatal flaw, but it does mean that the central control settings will not give the expected flat frequency response.

One cause of the problem is that some tone control circuits are passive types, and are therefore dependant on having suitable source and load impedances. Errors in either can cause unwanted changes in the responses of the controls. Figure 2.14 shows the circuit diagram for a simple passive tone control that will work reasonably well provided it is fed from a low source impedance and feeds into a reasonably high load impedance. Being a passive device it is not really correct to talk in terms of the controls providing boost and cut. The circuit always provides losses, and when set to provide bass or treble boost it is in fact providing reduced losses rather than a

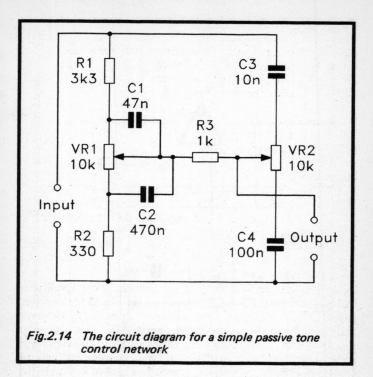

Fig.2.14   The circuit diagram for a simple passive tone control network

genuine boost to the signal level. This is not purely academic, and the system as a whole must be designed to take into account the basic loss of about 12dB through a circuit of this type.

My advice would be to not bother with passive circuits, and to instead opt for an active tone control circuit such as the one shown in the circuit diagram of Figure 2.15. This is basically just a passive tone control connected in the feedback circuit of a non-inverting amplifier, plus an input buffer stage to ensure that the main tone control circuit is driven from a suitably low source impedance. This gives a sort of inverted action, where boost from the tone controls gives more feedback and reduced gain, and cut from the controls gives less feedback and more gain. However, provided the tracks of the two potentiometers

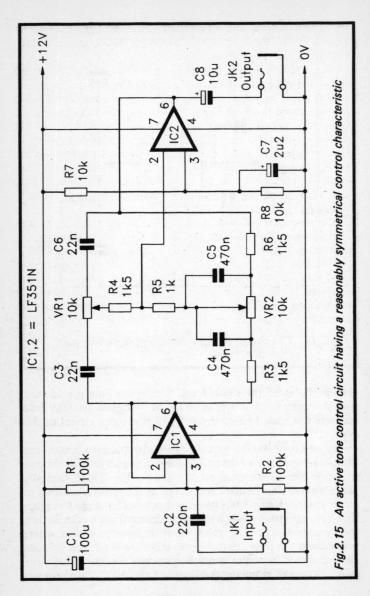

Fig.2.15 An active tone control circuit having a reasonably symmetrical control characteristic

78

are wired to take this into account, you will get the correct action from them (i.e. clockwise rotation giving boost; counter-clockwise rotation giving cut).

The circuit provides a little in excess of 12dB of boost and cut at the extremes of the audio range. Figure 2.16 shows the approximate frequency responses of the two controls when set for maximum boost and cut. These responses have quite good symmetry, and the circuit gives something very close to a flat response when the controls are set at the middle position. However, bear in mind that the tolerances of potentiometers are quite wide at about 20%, and that the mechanical mid-point is unlikely to be the true electrical mid-point. Any errors this produces in the supposedly flat frequency response should be quite minor though.

Construction of the tone controls presents no major difficulties. The voltage gain is so low, even when set for maximum boost, that there is no great risk of instability. Remember to get the tracks of the controls wired round the right way. Treble control VR1 provides boost with the wiper set towards the C3 end of the track, or cut with it set towards the C6 end. Similarly, bass control VR2 provides boost with the wiper set towards the R3 end of the track, or cut with it at the R6 end of the track. Note that there is a small voltage gain of about four or five times through the circuit at the 0dB reference level.

Components for Figure 2.14

Resistors (all 0.25 watt 5% carbon film)
R1   3k3
R2   330R
R3   1k

Potentiometers
VR1   10k lin carbon
VR2   10k lin carbon

Capacitors
C1   47n polyester 5% or better
C2   470n polyester 5% or better

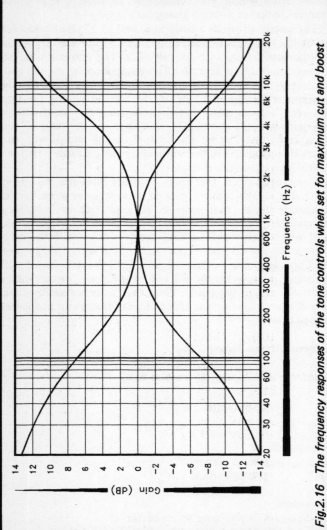

Fig.2.16 The frequency responses of the tone controls when set for maximum cut and boost

| C3 | 10n polyester 5% or better |
| C4 | 100n polyester 5% or better |

Miscellaneous
Two control knobs, wire, solder, etc.

Components for Figure 2.15

Resistors (all 0.25 watt 5% carbon film)
R1	100k
R2	100k
R3	1k5
R4	1k5
R5	1k
R6	1k5
R7	10k
R8	10k

Potentiometers
| VR1 | 10k lin carbon |
| VR2 | 10k lin carbon |

Capacitors
C1	100μ 25V elect
C2	220n polyester
C3	22n polyester 5% or better
C4	470n polyester 5% or better
C5	470n polyester 5% or better
C6	22n polyester 5% or better
C7	2μ2 63V elect
C8	10μ 50V elect

Semiconductors
| IC1 | LF351N |
| IC2 | LF351N |

Miscellaneous
| JK1 | standard jack socket |

JK2   standard jack socket
                Two 8 pin d.i.l. i.c. holders, circuit board, wire,
                solder, etc.

Loudness Filter

I always think that the name "loudness" filter is a rather inappropriate one for this type of filter. It is actually one that is for use when operating an audio system at low volume levels. It would therefore seem more apt to call it a "quietness" filter. Anyway, the idea of such a filter is that it should compensate for the seeming reduction in high and low frequency signals when listening at low volume levels. This is apparently due to the way the human hearing system operates, and the way in which the brain decodes the signals from the ears. The degree of boost needed is quite low, and most loudness filters provide only about 6dB or so of boost at bass frequencies, and somewhat less than this at high frequencies. A pair of ordinary bass and treble tone controls can actually provide suitable filtering, but a separate loudness filter provides a more convenient means of achieving much the same thing.

The circuit diagram of Figure 2.17 is for a simple loudness filter which provides about 6dB of boost at bass frequencies, and around 3dB to 4dB of boost at treble frequencies. Figure 2.18 shows the approximate frequency response of the circuit. The circuit is basically just a non-inverting amplifier with two types of frequency dependant negative feedback.

The bass boost is provided by C5 and R6. At most frequencies the impedance of C5 is low in comparison to that of R6, and R6 is therefore shunted across R5. At low frequencies the impedance of C5 becomes significant, and reduces the shunting effect of R6. This gives a higher feedback resistance, and somewhat boosted gain. The boost in gain is tamed by the inclusion of R5, which sets a suitable upper limit on the feedback impedance.

In the other section of the feedback network, R4 is shunted by R3, but only at high frequencies where C2 has a low impedance. This gives the high frequency boost, and R3 tames the response so that the required modest boost in gain is

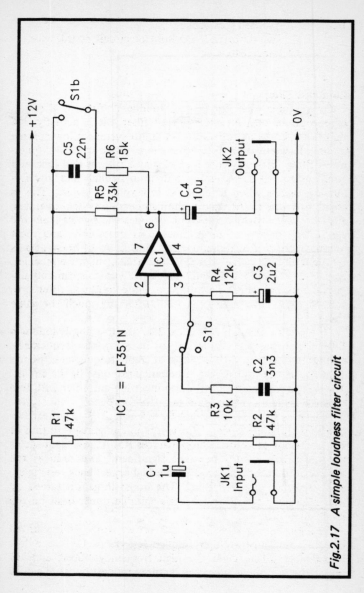

Fig.2.17 A simple loudness filter circuit

83

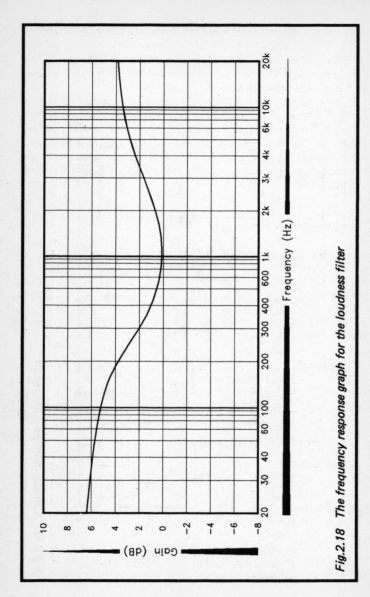

Fig.2.18 The frequency response graph for the loudness filter

produced. S1 enables the loudness filtering to be switched out without producing any significant change in the voltage gain at middle frequencies. S1a simply switches out R3 and C2 so that the high frequency boost is eliminated. S1b short circuits C5 so that R6 shunts R5 at all frequencies.

Once again, construction of this project should offer no real problems. The component layout is not critical. Although the circuit shows the unit as having input and output sockets, obviously it does not have to be built as a stand-alone unit. If it is built into an amplifier the input and output sockets are unnecessary. The same is true of most of the circuits featured in this book.

Components for Figure 2.17

Resistors (all 0.25 watt 5% carbon film)
R1	47k
R2	47k
R3	10k
R4	12k
R5	33k
R6	15k

Capacitors
C1	1μ 63V elect
C2	3n3 polyester
C3	2μ2 63V elect
C4	10μ 50V elect
C5	22n polyester

Semiconductor
IC1	LF351N

Miscellaneous
JK1	standard jack socket
JK2	standard jack socket
S1	d.p.d.t. toggle
	8 pin d.i.l. i.c. holder, circuit board, case, wire, solder, etc.

Mixers

Mostly it is only necessary to feed a power amplifier from one signal source at a time. A rotary or push-button switch assembly is used to select the required input socket, or the output from the appropriate preamplifier, and connect it through to the input of the power amplifier. Some applications require a mixer though. This is usually where the equipment must be fed from two sources simultaneously, such as a tape deck providing background music and a microphone preamplifier for the "live" commentary. Mixer inputs can also be used to give a sort of pseudo automatic input selection. Instead of selecting the appropriate signal source, you simply activate the one you require and it will be fed through to the power amplifier by the mixer stage.

Figure 2.19 shows the circuit diagram for a simple four input mixer. This is basically just an ordinary inverting amplifier circuit, but it has an input socket, input resistor, and d.c. blocking capacitor for each of four inputs. This is called a "summing mixer" circuit. The circuit operates much like a basic inverting mode amplifier, but the output must balance the sum of the input signals. It is from this summing action that this circuit configuration gets its name. This is actually the sort of circuit operational amplifiers were originally designed for, but using d.c. signals instead of a.c. types.

There is unity voltage gain from each input to the output, but the voltage gain could obviously be increased by making R7 higher in value. The voltage gain is set by feedback resistor values in normal inverting amplifier fashion. The input impedance is, of course, 100k at all four inputs.

Although the circuit is shown as having four inputs, in theory it is possible to have any desired number of inputs. Just add an input socket, coupling capacitor, and input resistor for each input you require. In practice there are limits on the number of inputs that can be used. There is no strict upper limit though — it depends on how much noise and distortion you are prepared to tolerate.

The first point to note is that each extra input reduces the performance of the circuit. Having (say) ten 100k input resistors is much the same as having one 10k input resistor. In other words, with ten inputs and unity voltage gain, the

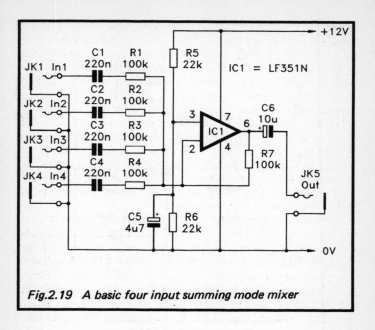

Fig.2.19 A basic four input summing mode mixer

operational amplifier has noise and distortion levels that are much the same as a circuit which has one input and a voltage gain of ten times. With the voltage gain at unity, you can obviously have quite a large number of inputs without the performance of the circuit dropping to an inadequate level. However, if you opt for a certain amount of voltage gain through the circuit, using a lot of inputs might not be acceptable. For instance, ten inputs plus a voltage gain of ten times gives the operational amplifier an effective voltage gain of 100 times. This is unlikely to give acceptable results. If you wish to have a large number of inputs, keep the voltage gain low.

In reality it is often not the effective gain of the operational amplifier that governs the maximum number of inputs that can be used. Having a large number of inputs tends to produce a lot of wiring at the input of the circuit, which in turn results in significant pick-up of mains "hum", etc. If you

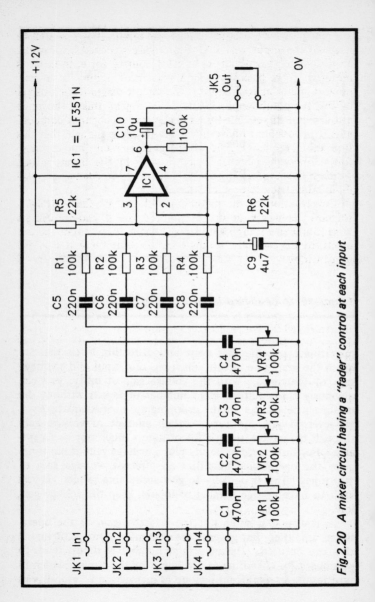

Fig.2.20 A mixer circuit having a "fader" control at each input

88

are going to have a large number of inputs it is essential to keep all the input wiring as thoroughly screened as possible.

If a mixer having an input level control for each input is required, it is basically just a matter of adding a "fader" potentiometer at each input. The circuit diagram for a mixer of this type is shown in Figure 2.20. Again, this is shown as a four-input mixer, but by adding extra sets of input components it is possible to have more inputs. Note though, that this type of mixer has much more wiring per input, and is therefore more vulnerable to stray pick-up in the input wiring. Adding the "faders" reduces the input impedance at each input from 100k to around 50k.

Construction of the mixer units should be fairly straightforward. However, as already pointed out, if you are using a large number of inputs the component and general layout needs to be carefully thought out so that there is minimal input wiring.

Components for Figure 2.19

Resistors (all 0.25 watt 5% carbon film)

R1	100k
R2	100k
R3	100k
R4	100k
R5	22k
R6	22k
R7	100k

Capacitors

C1	220n polyester
C2	220n polyester
C3	220n polyester
C4	220n polyester
C5	4μ7 63V elect
C6	10μ 50V elect

Semiconductor

IC1	LF351N

Miscellaneous

JK1	standard jack socket
JK2	standard jack socket
JK3	standard jack socket
JK4	standard jack socket
JK5	standard jack socket
	8 pin d.i.l. i.c. holder, circuit board, wire, solder, etc.

Components for Figure 2.20

Resistors (all 0.25 watt 5% carbon film)

R1	100k
R2	100k
R3	100k
R4	100k
R5	22k
R6	22k
R7	100k

Potentiometers

VR1	100k log carbon
VR2	100k log carbon
VR3	100k log carbon
VR4	100k log carbon

Capacitors

C1	470n polyester
C2	470n polyester
C3	470n polyester
C4	470n polyester
C5	220n polyester
C6	220n polyester
C7	220n polyester
C8	220n polyester
C9	$4\mu7$ 63V elect
C10	10μ 50V elect

Semiconductor

IC1	LF351N

Miscellaneous

JK1	standard jack socket
JK2	standard jack socket
JK3	standard jack socket
JK4	standard jack socket
JK5	standard jack socket
	Four control knobs, 8 pin d.i.l. i.c. holder, circuit board, wire, solder, etc.

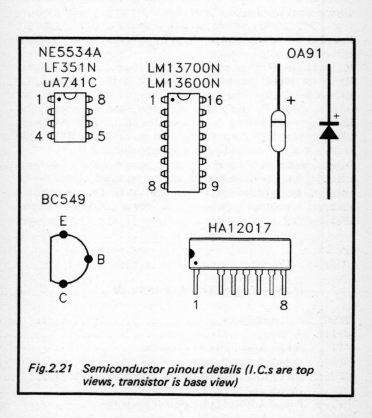

Fig.2.21 Semiconductor pinout details (I.C.s are top views, transistor is base view)

Also Available

HIGH POWER AUDIO AMPLIFIER CONSTRUCTION BP277
R. A. Penfold £3.95
▫ This book provides background information on high power audio amplifiers, together with some practical designs capable of output powers of up to around 300 to 400 watts r.m.s.
▫ The high power amplifier designs include types having power MOSFETS in the output stage. These give excellent performance over the full audio range, and offer good reliability from what are relatively simple circuits. Printed circuit designs are included for these power MOSFET circuits, as are suitable mains power supply designs.
▫ Using one of these power MOSFET amplifiers it is possible to obtain output powers of up to about 50 to 200 watts r.m.s. depending on the load impedance and the number of output devices used. By using two amplifiers (one inverting circuit and one non-inverting type) a bridge amplifier is produced, enabling very high output powers to be achieved (300 to 400 watts r.m.s. into a standard 8 ohm impedance load).
▫ For those who prefer to use bipolar output transistors, inverting and non-inverting circuits are provided. These can be used in single-ended or bridge configurations, and provide comparable output powers to the power MOSFET designs.
0 85934 222 0   1991   178 × 111mm   96 Pages

Other Titles of Interest